FLORIDA TREES and PALMS

TREES ARE PERMANENT
HOW TO CHOOSE AND GROW THEM

Cover picture is of *Tabebuia argentea*

Photography by
LEWIS S. MAXWELL

For information about our books refer to the back cover

LEWIS S. MAXWELL, Publisher
6230 Travis Boulevard
Tampa, Florida 33610

Manufactured in the United States of America

PREFACE

Over the years many people have expressed a desire for a book that would give them needed information on the selection and use of trees and palms in the Florida landscape.

Since trees are a permanent part of the landscape, careful thought should be given to their selection and location. It is very important that trees are chosen that will grow well in the location where they are desired.

This book pictures and describes many of the most suitable ornamental trees and larger palm trees for Florida. Some of the information includes: the approximate size of the mature tree, its cold and salt tolerances, pH preference, landscape use, flowering season, whether it is deciduous or evergreen, and its major problems. This book is arranged alphabetically according to the scientific names of the palms and then the other trees. The index consists of the common names of the trees and palms.

The proper placement of trees can save energy that otherwise would be used to heat or cool the home. About 20% to 30% of cooling and heating costs could be saved in this way. For instance, deciduous trees will give shade in the summer but permit the sun's rays to warm the home during the winter when it is beneficial.

Our thanks to Mr. Gene Joyner and Mr. Roger Newton, Extension Ornamental Horticulturists, for helping to find trees and palms to photograph and also for some of the information included in this book.

We cannot help you locate trees. Please consult your local nurseries or contact your local Cooperative Extension Agent for such information.

For the most part fruit trees are not included in this book because they can be found in our book *Florida Fruit*. The back cover of this book lists our companion books. These books are used in many Florida high schools, junior colleges, and vocational agricultural centers in their courses. A complete set of these books will answer most of your Florida gardening questions.

It is important to realize that gardening in Florida *is* different.

Lewis S. Maxwell

ISBN 0-9613240-1-5 >> $4.00

AUTHORS

Mr. Sylvester A. Rose, B.S.A., M.S.A.

Mr. Rose received his B.S. in Horticulture from the University of Rhode Island and his M.S. in Floriculture from Ohio State University. He has been both a Professor in Agriculture at Ohio University and a Horticulturist at the University of Florida.

He has owned and operated a retail flower shop in Ohio and in Florida. To add to this practical knowledge, he has worked for both a commercial greenhouse and a commercial landscaping organization.

Since 1956 he has lived in Florida. His knowledge and experience well qualify him to be an author of the book *Florida Flowers (Annuals and Bulbs)* and a book on Florida trees and palms.

Mr. Albert A. Will, Jr., B.L.A., M.S., U. of F.

Mr. Will is a graduate landscape architect and botanist turned teacher. He is known throughout south Florida, both for his horticultural lectures and for being the founder of the first two-year horticulture program in Florida at the Junior College of Broward County.

Mr. Will has appeared on both radio and TV, and he is an active member of many national and community professional horticultural societies. He is also a co-founder of the Broward County Bromeliad Society. He has taught numerous evening adult education courses in landscape design and plant identification and has been working "in plants" professionally since 1952.

His knowledge and experience well qualify him to be an author of the book *Florida Fruit* and a book on Florida trees and palms.

Professor Thomas B. Mack, B.S.A., M.Ed., U. of F.

Mr. Mack has taught landscape design at Florida Southern College at Lakeland for the last 32 years. A certified landscape architect, he has co-authored a number of books on gardening and has served as a newspaper columnist on landscaping.

Together with Dr. H. S. Wolfe and Professor John V. Watkins, Mr. Mack is co-author of the book *500 Answers to Your Florida Garden Questions* and the book *1001 Answers to Your Florida Garden Questions. Mr. Mack* is also co-author of *Florida Flowers (Annuals and Bulbs)* and *Florida Plant Selector.*

Mr. Lewis S. Maxwell, B.S.A., U. of F.

Mr. Maxwell is a professional entomologist and plant pathologist as well as an expert photographer.

He is the publisher of the *Florida Garden Guide,* a bimonthly publication, that is purchased by the better garden supply dealers, termite specialists, horticultural spraymen, and nurseries to give as a free service to their customers.

Companion gardening books to *Florida Trees and Palms* are his books *Florida Plant Selector, Florida Fruit, Florida Vegetables, Florida Flowers (Annuals and Bulbs), Florida Insects,* and *Florida Lawns and Gardens.*

CARE AND FEEDING OF TREES

by Lewis S. Maxwell

After you have chosen your tree and the place for it in your landscape, it is most important that the tree be well planted. What you do for a plant—any plant—before you plant it is more important than anything you can ever again do for that plant.

First, dig a large planting hole. Make it about three or four times as large as the tree's root ball. As you dig the hole, keep the top six to eight inches of topsoil separate from the subsoil. The topsoil is the best soil. Next, mix this topsoil with an equal volume of a composted cow manure and/or a quality peat. If the young tree is rootbound, cut into the root ball and spread the roots out in the planting hole. Plant the tree at the same height as it was previously growing. Place this mixture in the planting hole around the roots of the young tree. As you put this mixture in the hole use a hose to run water into the planting hole. This will eliminate any air pockets that might exist around the roots. Then use the subsoil to continue filling the hole, using the rest of the subsoil to make a saucer around the young tree. This will make watering easier.

Water the newly planted tree every third day for about two weeks. Then water it weekly until it is established. After that water it as needed.

Never put commercial mixed fertilizer into any planting hole as this has killed innumerable plants.

Wait until you see plant growth, and then start fertilizing the young tree with about a quarter to a half pound of a quality mixed fertilizer each feeding for the first year.

The **major** problem that trees have in Florida is hunger. I seldom see a tree that is not suffering in some degree from malnutrition. Trees should be fed with a quality mixed fertilizer containing added essential elements at least three times each year. Each application should be from one to ten pounds of fertilizer depending upon the size of the tree.

Palm trees should be fed with a quality palm special fertilizer three times each year. Use one pound for a small tree and up to eight pounds for a very large tree.

Essential element deficiencies are prevalent in Florida trees. Nitrogen deficiency is common. This appears as an overall yellowing of the foliage, especially of the older leaves. Also, growth is greatly retarded.

Magnesium deficiency is common in trees. Since magnesium is translocated within the tree, the first sign of this deficiency is chlorosis of the older leaves. The control is to make yearly applications of magnesium sulphate (epsom salts) at the rate of from one to five pounds depending upon the size of the tree.

Iron deficiency is sometimes a problem. This appears as a yellowing of the leaves with the veins remaining green. It can be corrected with applications of chelated iron.

Manganese is often deficient in palms, especially in the queen palm, royal palm, and the paurotis palm. This deficiency affects the new growth causing a frizzled look of the new leaves. The deficiency is called "frizzle-top." Depending upon the size of the palm, a yearly application of from one to three pounds of manganese sulphate will control this problem. It will take about six months for results to be seen. This deficiency is usually worse in alkaline soils.

It is also very important that weeds and grass are not allowed to grow near the young palm as they will greatly restrict its growth.

Be careful that you never injure the base of the palm with tools or lawn mowers, for these injuries will allow the entry of diseases such as butt rot, *Ganoderma,* into the palm. Also, you should not grow annual flowers against the base of a palm as this practice, because of the high humidity created, will make the palm more susceptible to fungus diseases.

Some pruning of palms is necessary. This consists mainly of removing old unsightly fronds and seed stalks.

Once your trees are established, they require very little care, except for fertilizing and watering, to remain healthy and beautiful.

Scientific Name *Acoelorrhaphe wrightii (Paurotis wrightii)* **Common Name** EVERGLADES PALM
PAUROTIS PALM
SAW CABBAGE PALM

Family Palmae **Approx. Height** 30′ **Width** 12′

Native to Coastal areas in S. Florida, West Indies, Mexico, and C. America.

Habit of Growth Multiple, slender, clustered trunks touching at base. Fiber leaf sheaths on trunks.

Description Leaves palmate, armed, deeply cut, with thin petiole bases that are undivided and have orange, saw-like teeth. Leaves medium to light green above, almost silvery below, to about 3′ wide.

Landscape Use Specimen, framing, border, avenue, and used with large rocks.

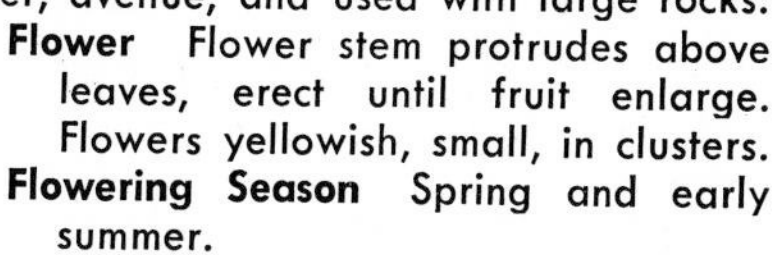

Flower Flower stem protrudes above leaves, erect until fruit enlarge. Flowers yellowish, small, in clusters.

Flowering Season Spring and early summer.

Fruit Black, roundish, to about ⅓″ across.

Soil & Moisture Tolerant of most soils. Best in moist soils. Will grow in brackish water or upland soils.

pH Preference 5.5 to 7.5.

Salt Tolerance Fair (2nd line).

Freezes at about 20°F.

Rate of Growth Moderate.

Propagation Seeds and division of clumps.

Culture Responds to fertilizer and Mn., Mg., and Fe. Remove some suckers, old fruiting stalks, and leaves.

Problems Leaf spot and root rot diseases. Palm-leaf skeletonizer. Manganese deficiency.

Scientific Name *Archontophoenix alexandrae* **Common Name** ALEXANDRA PALM

Family Palmae **Approx. Height** 45′ **Width** 12′

Native to Queensland, Australia.

Habit of Growth Single, slender, ringed trunk with somewhat swollen base.

Description Leaves pinnate, unarmed, stiffly arched, to 6′ long. Leaflets regularly arranged, to 2″ wide, dark green above and grayish below. Head looks like a feather duster. Prominent crownshaft.

Landscape Use Specimen, framing, avenue, pot or urn, and group plantings.

Flower Flower stem 3′ long, below crownshaft. Flowers whitish, numerous, small, in panicles.

Flowering Season Late spring.

Fruit Red, roundish, to about ½″ long.

Soil & Moisture Prefers enriched, well-drained soils.

pH Preference 5.5 to 7.0.

Salt Tolerance Fair (2nd line).

Freezes at about 30°F.

Rate of Growth Fast.

Propagation Seeds.

Culture Should be protected from strong winds.

Note: *A. cunninghamiana,* PICCABEEN or KING PALM, is somewhat similar and hardier.

Problems Leaf spot disease. Scale insects and palm aphids. Often shows minor element deficiency.

Scientific Name *Arecastrum romanzoffianum (Cocos plumosa)*

Common Name QUEEN PALM, PLUMY COCONUT PALM

Family Palmae

Approx. Height 50′ **Width** 15′

Native to South Brazil to Argentina.

Habit of Growth Single, tall, usually straight, gray-brown trunk, smooth but ringed by leaf scars. Old boots persist below leaves.

Description Leaves pinnate, unarmed, dark green, arching, feathery, to 15′ long with wide bases and long petioles. Midrib prominent. Leaflets many, to 3′ long and about 1 ½″ wide.

Landscape Use Specimen, framing, background, avenue, and group plantings.

Flower Showy inflorescence to 4′ long or more, below leaves. Flowers yellowish.

Flowering Season Summer.

Fruit Yellow to orange, roundish, about 1″ long.

Soil & Moisture Tolerant of most soils.

pH Preference 5.5 to 6.5.

Salt Tolerance Poor (3rd line).

Freezes at about 20° F.

Rate of Growth Moderate to fast.

Propagation Seeds.

Culture Feed two or three times a year with fertilizer containing 2% to 3% manganese. Yearly application of manganese sulphate 1 to 5 lbs. per tree.

Problems *Ganoderma* (butt rot) and false smut diseases. Scales. Manganese deficiency and high nitrogen requirement. Remove old leaves.

Scientific Name *Butia capitata* (*Cocos australis*)

Common Name PINDO PALM
JELLY PALM

Family Palmae

Approx. Height 20′ **Width** 10′

Native to Brazil.

Habit of Growth Single, stocky, grayish brown trunk to 1½′ in diameter with dense head. Leaf stalks persist.

Description Leaves pinnate, armed, curving, to 6′ long. Petioles have spines. Midrib prominent. Leaflets to about 2½′ long and to about 1″ wide, blue-green above and grayish below.

Landscape Use Specimen, avenue, and group plantings.

Flower Flower stem to 2½′ or more, among leaves. Flowers yellow to red.

Flowering Season Early summer.

Fruit Yellow to orange, roundish, about 1″ long. Sweet, edible pulp.

Soil & Moisture Tolerant of most well-drained soils.

pH Preference 5.5 to 6.5.

Salt Tolerance Fair (2nd line).

Freezes at about Hardy in Florida.

Rate of Growth Slow.

Propagation Seeds.

Culture Remove old leaves and seed spikes. Needs full sun.

Problems *Ganoderma* (palm butt rot) and false smut diseases. Palm-leaf skeletonizer and scales. Manganese deficiency.

Scientific Name *Caryota mitis* **Common Name** FISHTAIL PALM

Family Palmae **Approx. Height** 25′ **Width** 12′

Native to Tropical Asia and Malaya.

Habit of Growth Multiple, slender, ringed, brown trunks, to 4″ or more in diameter, produced by many basal suckers.

Description Leaves bipinnate, toothed, to 9′ long. Leaflets light green and resembling fish's tails.

Landscape Use Specimen, framing, border, patio, pot or urn, and avenue.

Flower Flower stem short, thick, with many branches, to 2′ long. It starts blooming at top of trunk and progresses down to base, then trunk dies.

Flowering Season All year.

Fruit Turns from red to black, roundish, ½″ across.

Soil & Moisture Prefers enriched, well-drained soil.

pH Preference 5.5 to 6.5.

Salt Tolerance Poor (3rd line).

Freezes at about 32°F.

Rate of Growth Moderate.

Propagation Seeds and division of clumps.

Culture When each trunk finishes flowering and fruiting, it will die and must be removed. Will grow in deep shade.

Problems Lethal yellowing disease. Scales. Mites. May blow over in high winds.

Scientific Name *Chamaedorea seifrizii* **Common Name** GRASS-LEAVED PARLOR PALM

Family Palmae **Approx. Height** 12′ **Width** 6′

Native to Central America.

Habit of Growth Multiple, upright, slender canes, about ¾″ in diameter, in clumps.

Description Leaves pinnate, unarmed, to 2′. Leaflets dark green, ¾″ wide, with terminal leaflets the same size as those below.

Landscape Use Specimen, hedge, patio, pot or urn, and indoor plantings.

Flower Inconspicuous. Flower stem to 12″, branched once, orange, among lower leaves. Dioecious.

Flowering Season Spring.

Fruit Green to black, roundish, ¼″ across.

Soil & Moisture Prefers moist, enriched, organic soil.

pH Preference 5.5 to 7.0.

Salt Tolerance Poor (3rd line).

Freezes at about 30°F.

Rate of Growth Moderate.

Propagation Seeds and division of clumps.

Culture Does well in shade but will take more sun than *C. erumpens*, BAMBOO PALM. *C. erumpens* has a terminal pair of leaflets to 3 times as wide as lower leaflets. There are many other species.

Problems Leaf spot disease. Scales and palm aphids. Mites. Nematodes.

Scientific Name *Chamaerops humilis* **Common Name** EUROPEAN FAN PALM

Family Palmae **Approx. Height** 4′-15′ **Width** 4′-8′

Native to Southern Europe.

Habit of Growth Multiple or single trunk, to about 1′ in diameter. Dead leaves may partially cover trunk.

Description Leaves palmate, armed, stiff, small, about 2′ to 3′ wide, deeply cut. Leaves vary in color from dark green, gray, to silvery. Petioles have spinose teeth. Usually persistent fibrous leaf sheaths.

Landscape Use Specimen, patio, pot or urn, and group plantings.

Flower Flower stem short, at top of trunk and hidden by foliage. Flowers borne singly.

Flowering Season Spring.

Fruit Red, yellow, or brown. Variable in size and shape. Fall.

Soil & Moisture Tolerant of most soils. Prefers enriched, well-drained soil.

pH Preference 5.5 to 8.0.

Salt Tolerance Fair (2nd line).

Freezes at about 20°F. Hardy in Florida.

Rate of Growth Slow.

Propagation Seeds and division of clumps.

Culture Likes cool weather. Water during dry periods.

Problems Lethal yellowing, *Ganoderma,* and leaf spot diseases. Ambrosia beetle and scales.

Scientific Name *Chrysalidocarpus lutescens* **Common Name** CANE PALM
(Some other names are:
MADAGASCAR PALM, BAMBOO PALM, YELLOW BUTTERFLY PALM)

Family Palmae **Approx. Height** 25′ **Width** 20′

Native to Madagascar.

Habit of Growth Multiple, erect, slender stems, green with bronze-yellow rings, to about 5″ in diameter, in clumps. Resembles bamboo.

Description Leaves pinnate, unarmed, graceful, ascending, curved at apex, to about 4′ to 6′ long. Petioles yellowish or orange tinged. Leaflets 40 to 60 pairs, yellow-green, about 1″ wide.

Landscape Use Specimen, framing, patio, pot or urn, and indoor plantings.

Flower Inflorescence among lower leaves.

Flowering Season Summer.

Fruit Yellow turning blackish, oblong, about ¾″ long. Fall.

Soil & Moisture Any enriched, moist soil.

pH Preference 5.5 to 7.5.

Salt Tolerance Poor (3rd line).

Freezes at about 32°F.

Rate of Growth Moderate.

Propagation Seeds and division of clumps.

Culture Needs adequate fertilizer to retain green foliage. Prune to remove dead leaves. Likes shade or will tolerate sun.

Problems Leaf spot and mushroom rot diseases. Scales.

Scientific Name *Coccothrinax argentata* **Common Name** FLORIDA SILVER PALM

Family Palmae **Approx. Height** 20′ **Width** 5′

Native to South Florida to the Bahamas.

Habit of Growth Single, slender trunk, to about 6″ in diameter, often short.

Description Leaves palmate, unarmed, 3′ wide. Dark green, glossy above and silvery below. Deeply cut with pendulous tips. Fibrous sheath.

Landscape Use Specimen, pot or urn.

Flower Flower stems to 2′ long, below leaves. Flowers white and small.

Flowering Season Spring.

Fruit Purple to black, round, to about ½″ across. Fall.

Soil & Moisture Tolerant of sand and lime rock soil.

pH Preference 6.0 to 8.0.

Salt Tolerance Excellent (1st line).

Freezes at about 28° F.

Rate of Growth Very slow.

Propagation Seeds. Difficult to transplant.

Culture Grows well on lime rock soils and partially shaded areas.

Problems Lethal yellowing and leaf spot diseases.

Scientific Name *Cocos nucifera* **Common Name** COCONUT PALM

Family Palmae **Approx. Height** *75′* **Width** *25′*

Native to Probably tropical Asia.

Habit of Growth Single, slender, often leaning, grayish brown trunk with rough leaf scars, bulbous base and dense head.

Description Leaves pinnate, unarmed, stiffly arched, to about 18′ long, with fibrous sheath. Leaflets many, to 3′ long and about 1 ½″ wide.

Landscape Use Specimen, framing, background, avenue, and group plantings.

Flower Flower stem to 4′, among lower leaves. Flowers creamy white, numerous, small.

Flowering Season Spring, summer, and warm months.

Fruit Yellowish green coconut turning brown, to about 1′ long. Edible.

Soil & Moisture Tolerant of many different soils. Prefers enriched soil with adequate moisture.

pH Preference *5.5* to *7.5*.

Salt Tolerance Excellent (1st line).

Freezes at about 32° F.

Rate of Growth Fast.

Propagation Seeds. Requires 3 to 6 months to sprout.

Culture No special care required. Malayan varieties require fertilization to look good.

Problems Lethal yellowing — Golden and other Malayan varieties resistant. *Ganoderma*, leaf spot, and bud rot diseases.

Scientific Name *Dictyosperma album*

Common Name PRINCESS PALM
HURRICANE PALM

Family Palmae

Approx. Height 30′ **Width** 15′

Native to Mascarene Islands.

Habit of Growth Single, straight, dark gray, ringed trunk with many vertical fissures, to about 8″ in diameter, and with swollen base.

Description Leaves pinnate, unarmed, shiny dark green, to 12′ long, with short petiole. Leaflets 50 or more pairs. Prominent, wide crownshaft.

Landscape Use Specimen, framing, patio, pot or urn.

Flower Flower stem drooping, to about 2′ long, below crownshaft. Flowers reddish yellow.

Flowering Season Summer.

Fruit Purple to black, nearly round, ½″ long. Fall.

Soil & Moisture Prefers enriched soil with adequate moisture.

pH Preference 5.5 to 7.5.

Salt Tolerance Fair (2nd line).

Freezes at about 30° F.

Rate of Growth Moderate.

Propagation Seeds. Difficult to transplant.

Culture Will grow in shade or sun. Withstands high winds. *D. album* var. *rubrum* has reddish veins when young.

Problems Lethal yellowing and leaf spot diseases. Palm aphids.

Scientific Name *Howea forsterana (Kentia forsterana)* **Common Name** FORSTER SENTRY PALM KENTIA PALM

Family Palmae **Approx. Height** 30′-60′ **Width** 12′

Native to Lord Howe Island (near Australia).

Habit of Growth Single, erect, smooth trunk with slightly raised leaf scars and a swollen base.

Description Leaves pinnate, unarmed, dark green, arching, to about 9′ long, with long petioles. Leaflets about 90, 2½′ long and 2″ wide. Weight of leaflets emerging from sides of midrib gives leaves a flat appearance.

Landscape Use Specimen, framing, patio, pot or urn, indoor plantings, and shady areas.

Flower Flower spikes 3 to 8, 3½′ long, among lower leaves.

Flowering Season Spring.

Fruit Yellow-green, ovoid, to 2″ long. Late summer.

Soil & Moisture Prefers enriched, well-drained, organic soil.

pH Preference 5.5 to 6.5.

Salt Tolerance Poor (3rd line).

Freezes at about 32° F.

Rate of Growth Moderate.

Propagation Seeds.

Culture Tolerant of shade.

Problems Leaf spot disease. Scales.

Scientific Name *Hyophorbe verschaffeltii* *(Mascarena verschaffeltii)* **Common Name** SPINDLE PALM PIGNUT PALM

Family Palmae **Approx. Height** 25′ **Width** 10′

Native to Mascarene Islands.

Habit of Growth Single, straight, smooth, gray-brown, stout trunk with leaf scars. Trunk bulges toward the top and has a compact head.

Description Leaves pinnate, unarmed, stiffly arched, to about 9′ long. Short petioles and prominent yellow-banded midribs. Leaflets are in several ranks. Pale green crownshaft.

Landscape Use Specimen, framing, border, pot or urn, and avenue.

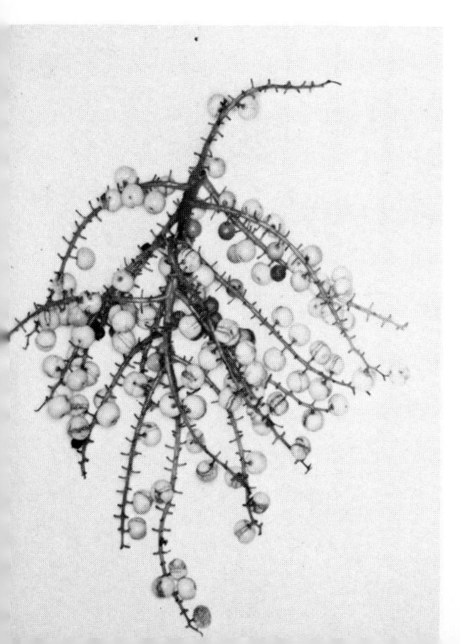

Flower Flower stem to about 1½′, at base of crownshaft. Flowers yellowish, in a 1′ long brush-like cluster.

Flowering Season Spring.

Fruit Black, oblong, about ¾″ long.

Soil & Moisture Prefers enriched soil with adequate moisture.

pH Preference 5.5 to 7.5.

Salt Tolerance Fair (2nd line).

Freezes at about 30° F.

Rate of Growth Moderate.

Propagation Seeds.

Culture Easy to grow. Thrives in sun or shade. Remove old leaves and old seed stalks. Mulch area around palm.

Problems Lethal yellowing and leaf spot diseases.

Scientific Name *Latania lontaroides* *(L. commersonii)* *(L. borbonica)*

Common Name RED LATAN PALM

Family Palmae

Approx. Height 35′ **Width** 15′

Native to Mascarene Islands.

Habit of Growth Single, straight, gray, stout trunk with swollen base and complete, wide, bulging ring-scars. No fiber in the crown.

Description Leaves palmate, armed, stiff, gray-green, to 12′ with blade 5′ to 8′ wide. Long petioles and midribs tinged red when young. Petioles have sharp teeth when young.

Landscape Use Specimen and framing.

Flower Flower stem 3′ to 6′, among leaves. Dioecious.

Flowering Season Spring.

Fruit Yellow-green to glossy brown, roundish, to about 2″ in diameter. Fall.

Soil & Moisture Well-drained, enriched soil.

pH Preference 5.5 to 7.5.

Salt Tolerance Fair (2nd line).

Freezes at about 28° F.

Rate of Growth Slow.

Propagation Seeds.

Culture Male and female plants must be close to each other for fruit to form.

Problems No serious pests.

Scientific Name *Livistona chinensis* **Common Name** CHINESE FAN PALM
CHINESE FOUNTAIN PALM

Family Palmae **Approx. Height** 25′ **Width** 12′

Native to China.

Habit of Growth Single, straight, stout trunk with incomplete leaf scars and a compact, rounded head with much fiber in its crown.

Description Leaves palmate, armed. Petiole long, with small, recurving, short spines on lower half. Leaf blade olive green, 3′ to 6′ across, deeply cut, with tips hanging sharply downward on older plants.

Landscape Use Specimen, framing, pot or urn, avenue, and group plantings.

Flower Flower stem to 6′, among leaves. Flowers greenish, small, in long clusters.

Flowering Season Spring and summer.

Fruit Greenish blue, ovoid, to 1″ long. Fall.

Soil & Moisture Enriched, well-drained soil.

pH Preference 5.5 to 6.5.

Salt Tolerance Fair (2nd line).

Freezes at about Hardy in most of Florida.

Rate of Growth Moderate.

Propagation Seeds.

Culture Prune to remove old leaves. Prefers shade when young.

Problems Lethal yellowing, leaf spot, and false smut diseases. Scales.

Scientific Name *Phoenix canariensis* **Common Name** CANARY ISLAND DATE PALM
CANARY DATE PALM

Family Palmae **Approx. Height** 50′ **Width** 25′

Native to Canary Islands.

Habit of Growth Single, straight, massive trunk, 2′ to 4′, with diamond pattern from leaf scars on trunk and a dense head.

Description Leaves pinnate, armed, arched, 15′ to 20′ long. Petioles have long, sharp spines. Leaflets numerous, dull green, stiff.

Landscape Use Specimen, background, avenue, and park. Too large for average homegrounds.

Flower Flower stem about 3′, among leaves. Flowers yellowish, small, in clusters. Dioecious.

Flowering Season Spring to summer.

Fruit Yellow to orange, ovoid, ¾″ long, ½″ wide.

Soil & Moisture Prefers enriched, well-drained soil.

pH Preference 5.5 to 6.5.

Salt Tolerance Fair (2nd line).

Freezes at about Hardy in Florida.

Rate of Growth Slow.

Propagation Seeds.

Culture Needs fertilizer and extra magnesium. Wind resistant.

Problems Lethal yellowing, leaf spot, and false smut diseases. Palm weevil, palm leaf skeletonizer, and scales. Mites.

Scientific Name *Phoenix reclinata*

Common Name SENEGAL DATE PALM
CLUSTER DATE PALM

Family Palmae

Approx. Height 35′ **Width** 50′

Native to Tropical Africa.

Habit of Growth Multiple (as many as 20 or more), slender, about 6″ to 8″ wide, gracefully curving trunks with leaf scars and dense heads.

Description Leaves pinnate, armed, spreading, to 9′ or more. Petioles orange with long, sharp spines at the base. Leaflets dark green, stiff, about 15″ long.

Landscape Use Specimen, framing, and background.

Flower Flower stem to about 3′, among leaves. Flowers creamy-white. Dioecious.

Flowering Season Spring to summer.

Fruit Orange-red, ovoid, about ¾″. Fall.

Soil & Moisture Prefers enriched, well-drained soil.

pH Preference 5.5 to 6.5.

Salt Tolerance Fair (2nd line).

Freezes at about 24°F.

Rate of Growth Fast for a palm.

Propagation Seeds and division of clumps.

Culture Remove old leaves and old seed spikes.

Problems Lethal yellowing, leaf spot, and false smut diseases. Palm leaf skeletonizer. Magnesium deficiency.

Scientific Name *Pritchardia pacifica* **Common Name** FIJI FAN PALM

Family Palmae **Approx. Height** 30′ **Width** 10′

Native to Fiji Islands.

Habit of Growth Single, straight, smooth trunk, about 1′ wide, fan palm.

Description Leaves palmate, unarmed, to 8′, with petiole up to 3′. Blades bright green, stiff, to 5′ long and 4′ wide, shallowly cut, with up to 90 attractively pleated segments.

Landscape Use Specimen, framing, pot or urn, avenue, and group plantings.

Flower Flower stem to 3′ long, among and shorter than leaves. Flowers bisexual, clustered at tips.

Flowering Season Summer.

Fruit Black, globular, ½″ across.

Soil & Moisture Enriched, well-drained soil.

pH Preference 5.5 to 7.5.

Salt Tolerance Fair (2nd line).

Freezes at about 32°F.

Rate of Growth Slow.

Propagation Seeds.

Culture Prefers partial shade. Another species *P. thurstonii* has flower stems that hang down below the leaves.

Problems Lethal yellowing and leaf spot diseases. Scales. Mites. Can be damaged by strong winds.

Scientific Name *Ptychosperma elegans* **Common Name** SOLITAIRE PALM

Family Palmae **Approx. Height** 20′ **Width** 10′

Native to Queensland, Australia.

Habit of Growth Single, straight, slender, ringed, gray trunk to 4″ in diameter, with raised leaf scars and swollen base.

Description Leaves pinnate, unarmed, stiffly arched, to 8′ long. Midrib prominent. Leaflets about 58, to 2½′ long and 4″ wide, bright green above and gray below. Prominent, slender, green crownshaft.

Landscape Use Specimen, framing, patio, pot or urn, and group plantings. Ideal for limited space as in small homegrounds.

Flower Flower stem to about 2′, below crownshaft. Flowers whitish, in bushy clusters.

Flowering Season Spring to summer.

Fruit Red, ovoid, ¾″ long, in showy sprays. Summer to early winter.

Soil & Moisture Enriched, well-drained soil.

pH Preference 5.5 to 7.5.

Salt Tolerance Fair (2nd line).

Freezes at about 30°F.

Rate of Growth Moderate.

Propagation Seeds.

Culture Easily grown. Tolerant of shade.

Problems *Ganoderma* and leaf spot diseases.

Scientific Name *Ptychosperma macarthurii* **Common Name** MACARTHUR PALM

Family Palmae **Approx. Height** 20′ **Width** 12′

Native to New Guinea.

Habit of Growth Multiple, slender, ringed, light gray trunks, about 3″ in diameter, with raised leaf scars, in clumps.

Description Leaves pinnate, unarmed, to about 6′ long. Midrib prominent. Leaflets to about 2″ wide with jagged tips. Prominent crownshaft.

Landscape Use Specimen, framing, pot or urn, and avenue.

Flower Flower stem to 2′, below crownshaft. Flowers whitish, in clusters.

Flowering Season Spring.

Fruit Red, ovoid, ½″ to ¾″ long, in showy sprays. Summer.

Soil & Moisture Most well-drained soils.

pH Preference 5.5 to 7.5.

Salt Tolerance Fair (2nd line).

Freezes at about 32°F.

Rate of Growth Moderate.

Propagation Seeds.

Culture Easily grown. Tolerant of shade.

Problems *Ganoderma* and leaf spot diseases. Palm aphids and scales.

Scientific Name *Roystonea regia*

Common Name CUBAN ROYAL PALM

Family Palmae

Approx. Height *70′* **Width** *25′*

Native to Cuba.

Habit of Growth Single, majestic, upright, smooth, faintly ringed, gray-white trunk, often enlarged at base and swollen near the middle, tapering toward the crownshaft. Drooping lower leaves form almost globose head.

Description Leaves pinnate, unarmed, arched, bright green, to 15′ long. Midrib prominent. Leaflets to 3′ long, 1″ to 1½″ wide, with secondary ribs. Prominent, long, bright green crownshaft.

Landscape Use Specimen, framing large buildings, avenue, and large, open areas.

Flower Flower stem below crownshaft. Flowers small.

Flowering Season Spring to summer.

Fruit Dark red to purple, oblongish, about ½″ long.

Soil & Moisture Adaptable. Tolerates wet soils (brackish). Prefers enriched, moist, well-drained soil.

pH Preference 5.5 to 8.0.

Salt Tolerance Fair (2nd line).

Freezes at about 28°F.

Rate of Growth Fast.

Propagation Seeds.

Culture Wind resistant. Note: *R. elata* is native to south Florida and is quite similar.

Problems Leaf spot disease. Royal palm bug and scales. Manganese deficiency.

Scientific Name *Sabal palmetto* **Common Name** CABBAGE PALM
CABBAGE PALMETTO

Family Palmae **Approx. Height** 80′ **Width** 12′

Native to North Carolina to Florida and the Bahamas.

Habit of Growth Single, straight, stout, rough, brown trunk, usually with old leaf bases until it is old and becomes bare and gray. Rounded, compact head. Specimens with branched trunks are rarely seen in Florida.

Description Leaves palmate, unarmed, dull green, stiff, to about 7′ long, deeply cut. Petiole stout, to 7′ long, extends into leaf blade curving sharply downward.

Landscape Use Specimen, framing, background, skyline, avenue, group plantings.

Flower Flower stem long, slender, drooping, with numerous branches, among and as long as the leaves. Flowers whitish, about 1/4″ wide.

Flowering Season Summer.

Fruit Black, rounded, to 1/2″ in diameter.

Soil & Moisture Tolerant of most soils.

pH Preference 5.0 to 8.0.

Salt Tolerance Excellent (1st line).

Freezes at about Hardy.

Rate of Growth Slow.

Propagation Seeds. Transplants easily during the growing season.

Culture Remove old leaves and seed stalks. Note: It is the State tree of Florida and protected by State law.

Problems Leaf spot disease. Palm weevil and scales.

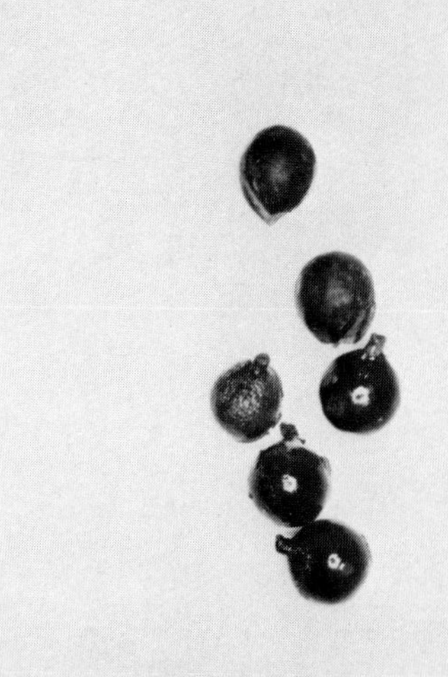

Scientific Name *Thrinax radiata (T. floridana)* **Common Name** FLORIDA THATCH PALM

Family Palmae **Approx. Height** 30′ **Width** 9′

Native to South Florida, Bahamas, West Indies, and Caribbean area.

Habit of Growth Single, slender, rough trunk, to about 6″ in diameter, becoming smooth with age.

Description Leaves palmate, unarmed. Petiole split at base. Leaves to about 3′ long, shining above, dull green below. Tips of leaves bent downward. Fibers occur at the base of the leaf stems.

Landscape Use Specimen, pot or urn, and group plantings. Good for small homegrounds.

Flower Flower stem to about 4′, usually appears above leaves. Flowers white, small.

Flowering Season Late spring and summer.

Fruit Whitish, soft, globose with short stem, to about 1/4″. Fall.

Soil & Moisture Well adapted to south Florida.

pH Preference 5.5 to 7.0.

Salt Tolerance Excellent (1st line).

Freezes at about 30°F.

Rate of Growth Moderate.

Propagation Seeds.

Culture Easily grown. Sometimes confused with *T. microcarpa* which has a thicker trunk, to 8″ in diameter, and leaves that are silvery below.

Problems Leaf spot disease.

Scientific Name *Trachycarpus fortunei*

Common Name WINDMILL PALM
CHINESE WINDMILL PALM

Family Palmae

Approx. Height 30′ **Width** 12′

Native to Asia.

Habit of Growth Single, straight, slender trunk with remnants of black, hairlike fibers at old leaf bases and a compact head.

Description Leaves palmate, almost round, stiff, gray-green, 2′ to 4′ wide, deeply cut. Petioles long, slender, not divided, finely toothed along margins.

Landscape Use Specimen, framing, pot or urn, and group plantings. A moderately small palm.

Flower Flower stem to 1½′ long, among leaves. Flowers white to yellow.

Flowering Season Summer.

Fruit Bluish, glossy, kidney-shaped, ½″ wide. Winter.

Soil & Moisture Enriched, well-drained soil.

pH Preference 5.5 to 6.5.

Salt Tolerance Fair (2nd line).

Freezes at about Hardy in Florida.

Rate of Growth Slow.

Propagation Seeds.

Culture Needs fertilizer and water.

Problems Lethal yellowing disease. Not suitable for south Florida.

Scientific Name *Veitchia merrillii (Adonidia merrillii)*

Common Name MANILA PALM
CHRISTMAS PALM

Family Palmae

Approx. Height 25′ **Width** 10′

Native to Philippine Islands.

Habit of Growth Single, erect, narrowly ringed trunk, to 10″ in diameter, with a swollen base.

Description Leaves pinnate, unarmed, stiffly arched, somewhat recurved, to 6′ long. Prominent midrib. Leaflets about 100, pale green, to 2½′ long and 2″ wide. Prominent, thick, green crownshaft.

Landscape Use Specimen, framing, patio, pot or urn, avenue, and group plantings. Good for small homegrounds.

Flower Flower stem short, below crownshaft. Flowers creamy white, small, in branched clusters.

Flowering Season Summer.

Fruit Very showy, bright red, ovoid, pointed, 1″ to 1½″ long. Winter and spring.

Soil & Moisture Tolerant of lime rock and moist soils.

pH Preference 6.5 to 8.0.

Salt Tolerance Fair (2nd line).

Freezes at about 30°F.

Rate of Growth Moderate.

Propagation Seeds.

Culture Provide partial shade to young plants.

Problems Lethal yellowing and leaf spot diseases. Scales.

Scientific Name *Washingtonia robusta* **Common Name** WASHINGTON PALM
MEXICAN WASHINGTON PALM

Family Palmae **Approx. Height** 80′ **Width** 10′-15′

Native to Mexico and southern California.

Habit of Growth Single, straight, slender, pale gray trunk, tapered from a stout base, often covered by old leaves. Close, compact head.

Description Leaves palmate, armed, bright green, to about 5′ wide, with drooping tips. Petioles reddish brown, about 3′ long, with spines on margins especially when young.

Landscape Use Background, avenue, and parks. Close to tall buildings.

Flower Flower stalk to 12′, among and exceeding leaves. Flowers whitish, small, in branched clusters.

Flowering Season Spring.

Fruit Black, roundish, about ⅓″ long. Fall.

Soil & Moisture Tolerant of most soils. Prefers moderately good, well-drained soil.

pH Preference 5.0 to 7.0.

Salt Tolerance Fair (2nd line).

Freezes at about 20°F.

Rate of Growth Fast once established.

Propagation Seeds.

Culture Requires little attention.

Problems Leaf spot and false smut diseases. Palm leaf skeletonizer and scales. Too tall for small lots.

Scientific Name *Acacia auriculiformis* **Common Name** EARLEAF ACACIA

Family Leguminosae **Approx. Height** 50′ **Width** 45′

Native to Australia.

Habit of Growth Upright tree with short trunk and rounded head.

Description Flattened, light green, modified petioles are leaf-like, slightly sickle-shaped, and 4″ to 7″ long. Seedlings have true leaves.

Landscape Use Specimen, framing, background, shade, and avenue.

Flower Yellow, button-like, in spikes 2″ to 3″ long.

Flowering Season Early spring and fall.

Fruit Flat pod, curved at maturity, to 4″ long. Black seeds.

Soil & Moisture Any well-drained soil. Does well on poor soils.

pH Preference 5.5 to 7.5.

Salt Tolerance Fair (2nd line).

Freezes at about 28° F.

Rate of Growth Fast.

Propagation Seeds. Fresh seeds sprout readily.

Culture No special care required. Tolerates neglect.

Problems Twig blight and root rot diseases. Stem borers. Wood is brittle and damaged by strong winds.

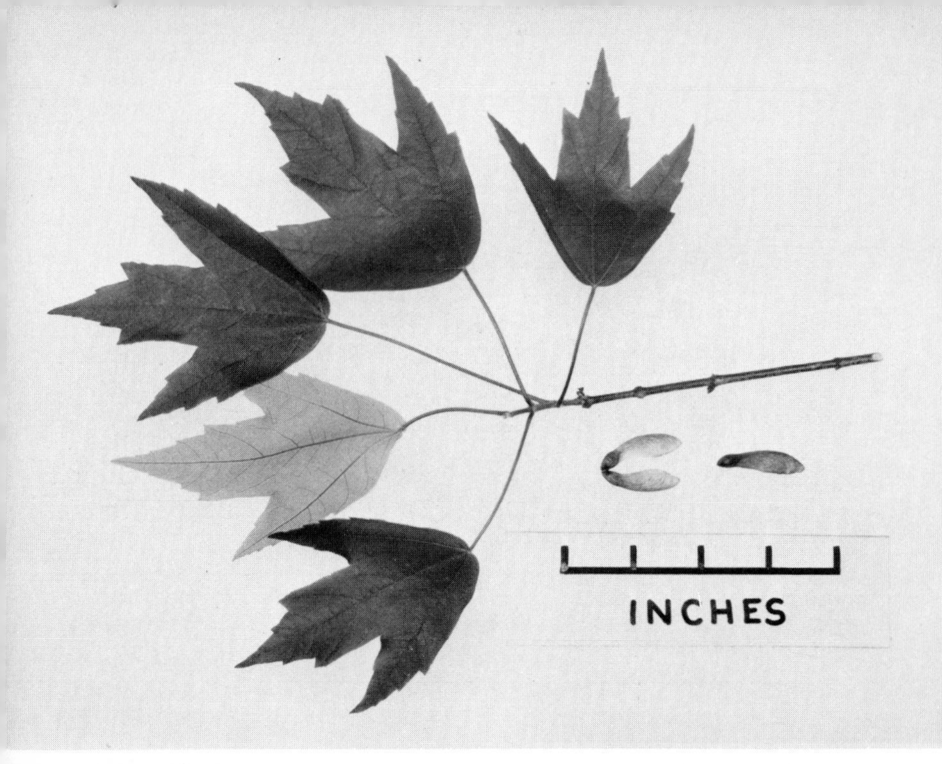

Scientific Name *Acer rubrum* **Common Name** RED MAPLE

Family Aceraceae **Approx. Height** *75′* **Width** *45′*

Native to Eastern North America to Texas.

Habit of Growth Dense, upright tree.

Description Leaves deciduous, opposite, simple, palmately 3 to 5-lobed, serrate, to 4″ long. Green above and pale green below with red petiole. Leaves turn yellow, orange, and red with cold weather.

Landscape Use Specimen, framing, skyline, shade, and avenue. Seasonal color.

Flower Reddish, in clusters, appearing before leaves.

Flowering Season Winter.

Fruit Reddish, winged samara. January and February.

Soil & Moisture Prefers enriched, moist, acid soil.

pH Preference 5.5 to 7.0.

Salt Tolerance Poor (3rd line).

Freezes at about Hardy.

Rate of Growth Moderate to fast.

Propagation Seeds. Young seedlings require good care. Better clones from cuttings.

Culture A woods tree. Use in wet situations. Root area should not be disturbed and should be mulched. Tree requires several years to become established.

Problems Leaf scorch is common in dry soils. Leaf spot disease. Twig borers. Mites.

Scientific Name *Albizia julibrissin* **Common Name** MIMOSA TREE SILK TREE

Family Leguminosae **Approx. Height** 30′ **Width** 35′

Native to Asia.

Habit of Growth Medium, low tree with a short trunk and horizontally spreading branches.

Description Leaves deciduous, even bipinnately compound, to 8″. Leaflets opposite, light green, fine, feather-like, to ¼″. Small twigs arise from upper portion of the limbs. None grow downward.

Landscape Use Patio. For light shade or any spot in the landscape where a medium sized tree is desirable. Use for flower color.

Flower Pink, powder-puff clusters.

Flowering Season Spring to June.

Fruit Tan pod to 6″ long, under 1″ wide.

Soil & Moisture Most well-drained soils.

pH Preference 5.5 to 8.0.

Salt Tolerance Poor (3rd line).

Freezes at about Hardy.

Rate of Growth Fast.

Propagation Seeds, graftings, and root cuttings. There is a wilt-resistant variety.

Culture Grows with little care.

Problems Wilt disease. Scales and treehoppers. Mites.

Scientific Name *Albizia lebbeck* **Common Name** WOMAN'S-TONGUE-TREE

Family Leguminosae **Approx. Height** *50′* **Width** *50′*

Native to Tropical Asia and north Australia.

Habit of Growth Large tree with pale bark and wide-spreading branches.

Description Leaves deciduous, even bipinnately compound, to 15″ long. Leaflets opposite, pale green, oblongish, to about 1½″. Petioles with oval gland near base.

Landscape Use Background. Use when fast growing tree is desired. Not recommended for small homegrounds.

Flower Greenish yellow balls, 2″ to 3″ across, in clusters.

Flowering Season Spring.

Fruit Tan, flat, thin pod, to 12″ long. Oval seeds.

Soil & Moisture Most any soil; drought resistant.

pH Preference 5.5 to 7.5.

Salt Tolerance Fair (2nd line).

Freezes at about 25°F.

Rate of Growth Fast.

Propagation Seeds grow rather easily.

Culture No special care required.

Problems Scales. Mites. Plant has naturalized itself in south Florida; a weed tree. Seed pods rattle when wind blows. Strong winds break branches. Widely spreading roots. Leaves and seed pods are a nuisance.

Scientific Name *Araucaria heterophylla (A. excelsa)* **Common Name** NORFOLK ISLAND PINE

Family Araucariaceae **Approx. Height** 60′ **Width** 20′

Native to Norfolk Island.

Habit of Growth Pyramidal tree with horizontal, symmetrical branches arranged in tiers.

Description Leaves evergreen, dark green, short, stiff, sharp-pointed, needle-like, about ½″ long.

Landscape Use Specimen. Potted specimen when young. Background for planting in coastal areas.

Flower Inconspicuous.

Flowering Season Spring.

Fruit Roundish, woody cone, 3″ to 5″ wide with spiny scales. Fall.

Soil & Moisture Enriched, well-drained soils.

pH Preference 5.5 to 7.0.

Salt Tolerance Fair (2nd line).

Freezes at about 24°F. Damaged at 30°F.

Rate of Growth Medium to fast.

Propagation Seeds and cuttings from terminal tips of mature wood for symmetrical plants. Mist soft wood cuttings in summer. Florida seeds have poor viability.

Culture Responds to fertilizer. Should be mulched.

Problems Blight disease of lower branches. Scales. Mites. Wind may break top.

Scientific Name *Bauhinia blakeana* **Common Name** HONG KONG BAUHINIA
HONG KONG ORCHID TREE

Family Leguminosae **Approx. Height** 30′ **Width** 25′

Native to Southeastern Asia.

Habit of Growth Bushy, spreading tree with long branches.

Description Leaves simple, deeply cut into two rounded lobes, coarse, to 8″ wide.

Landscape Use Specimen and avenue. Wherever a small to medium tree is needed. Winter color.

Flower Rose-purple, orchid-like, to 6″ wide.

Flowering Season October to March.

Fruit None in Florida.

Soil & Moisture Tolerant of most soils. Flowers best on dry soils. Deciduous on dry soils.

pH Preference 5.5 to 7.0.

Salt Tolerance Fair (2nd line).

Freezes at about 30°F.

Rate of Growth Fast.

Propagation Cuttings, graftings, and air layerings.

Culture Long branches should be pruned to shape. Often chlorotic—needs extra essential elements.

Problems Leaf spot and leaf scorch diseases. Caterpillars. Mites.

Scientific Name *Bauhinia purpurea* **Common Name** ORCHID TREE

Family Leguminosae **Approx. Height** 30′ **Width** 30′

Native to Asia.

Habit of Growth Tree with slender trunk, wide head, and drooping branches.

Description Leaves deciduous (from February to April), simple, deeply cut into two rounded lobes, coarse, to 6″ wide. Blooms while leaves are on the tree.

Landscape Use Specimen, framing, background, and avenue. Seasonal color.

Flower Color variable: red, pink, lavender, or white, orchid-like, to 5″ wide. Petals narrow.

Flowering Season Autumn (September to November).

Fruit Brown, slender, flat pod to 1′ long.

Soil & Moisture Tolerant of most soils. Flowers best on dry soils.

pH Preference 5.5 to 7.0.

Salt Tolerance Fair (2nd line).

Freezes at about 26°F.

Rate of Growth Fast to moderate.

Propagation Seeds, cuttings, and air layerings.

Culture Often chlorotic - needs extra essential elements. Prune to shape.

Problems Leaf spot and leaf scorch diseases. Caterpillars. Mites. Seedlings can be a problem.

Scientific Name *Bauhinia variegata*

Common Name ORCHID TREE
MOUNTAIN EBONY

Family Leguminosae

Approx. Height 25′ **Width** 20′

Native to Southeastern Asia.

Habit of Growth Tree with short trunk and long, slender, lateral branches.

Description Leaves deciduous, simple, deeply cut into two rounded lobes, coarse, light green, to 5″ wide.

Landscape Use Specimen, background, and avenue. Wherever a small to medium tree is needed. Seasonal color.

Flower Lavender to dark purple, orchid-like, to 4″ wide. Petals obovate. Fragrant.

Flowering Season Spring, before many leaves.

Fruit Brown, narrow, flat pod to 1′ long.

Soil & Moisture Tolerant of most soils. Flowers best on dry soils.

pH Preference 5.5 to 7.0.

Salt Tolerance Fair (2nd line).

Freezes at about 26°F.

Rate of Growth Moderate to fast.

Propagation Seeds, cuttings, and air layerings. Cv. 'Candida' has white flowers.

Culture Often chlorotic—needs extra essential elements. Prune to shape.

Problems Leaf spot, leaf scorch, and mushroom root rot diseases. Caterpillars. Mites.

Scientific Name *Bischofia javanica* **Common Name** BISHOPWOOD TOOG

Family Euphorbiaceae **Approx. Height** 60′ **Width** 40′

Native to Tropical Asia.

Habit of Growth Tree with a dense, spreading crown.

Description Leaves evergreen, alternate, compound with 3 oval leaflets to 8″ long, pointed and edged with fine serrations. Leaves turn red and drop during droughts. Milky sap.

Landscape Use Specimen and background. Shade tree when quick, dense shade is required.

Flower Greenish-yellow, small, in clusters. Dioecious. Fragrant.

Flowering Season Late winter and spring.

Fruit Brownish black, round, ⅓″ wide. Summer.

Soil & Moisture Tolerant to most soils.

pH Preference 5.5 to 8.0.

Salt Tolerance Fair (2nd line).

Freezes at about 26°F.

Rate of Growth Fast.

Propagation Seeds and cuttings. Let base of cuttings dry before planting.

Culture Little care required after it is established.

Problems Scales and whiteflies. Sensitive to Atrazine. Difficult to grow a lawn under its dense shade. Can become a weed tree. Weak branches. Leaves and fruit are a nuisance.

Scientific Name *Brassaia actinophylla* *(Schefflera actinophylla)*

Common Name QUEENSLAND UMBRELLA-TREE
OCTOPUS TREE
SCHEFFLERA

Family Araliaceae

Approx. Height 40′ **Width** 20′

Native to Australia.

Habit of Growth Upright, small to medium tree with green bark.

Description Leaves evergreen, palmately compound. Petioles to 2′. Leaflets shiny, light green, oblanceolate, to 1′ long.

Landscape Use Specimen, framing, patio, pot or urn, and tropical effect.

Flower Showy, terminal branching, red racemes above the foliage.

Flowering Season Summer and early fall.

Fruit Purplish black, round, fleshy drupe to 1/4″.

Soil & Moisture Tolerant of most soils. Does not like wet feet.

pH Preference 5.5 to 8.0.

Salt Tolerance Fair (2nd line).

Freezes at about 29°F. Will come back.

Rate of Growth Moderate to fast.

Propagation Seeds, cuttings, and air layerings.

Culture Easy to grow. Responds well to fertilizer. Prune severely to keep in shape.

Problems Bacterial leaf spot disease. Scales and aphids. Nematodes. Oedema. Spreading surface root system. Leaves and fruit are a nuisance.

Scientific Name *Bucida buceras* **Common Name** BLACK OLIVE

Family Combretaceae **Approx. Height** 40′-60′ **Width** 40′-60′

Native to South Florida, Bahamas, West Indies, and Central America.

Habit of Growth Upright tree with broadly rounded head. Branches droop near the ends.

Description Leaves mostly evergreen, simple, leathery, oblanceolate, to 3½″ long, in whorls near the tips of the twigs. A very beautiful, graceful tree.

Landscape Use Framing, shade, avenue, seaside, and windbreak.

Flower Greenish white, small, on spikes near the tips of twigs.

Flowering Season Late spring.

Fruit Oval, fuzzy, drupe about ⅓″ long.

Soil & Moisture Grows well on dry soils. Tolerates drought.

pH Preference 5.5 to 8.5.

Salt Tolerance Excellent (1st line).

Freezes at about 30°F.

Rate of Growth Moderate.

Propagation Cuttings and air layerings. Seeds germinate poorly as few trees produce quantities of viable seeds.

Culture Easy to grow. Responds to fertilizer and care. *Bucida spinosa* is a popular DWARF BLACK OLIVE.

Problems Leaf spot disease. Scales and whiteflies. Mites. Galls.

Scientific Name *Bursera simaruba* **Common Name** GUMBO-LIMBO
GUM ELEMI

Family Burseraceae **Approx. Height** 60′ **Width** 40′

Native to South Florida, Bahamas, West Indies, and Central America.

Habit of Growth Tree with thick trunk and odd, light reddish brown, flaking bark, colorful when leafless.

Description Leaves deciduous, clustered, pinnately compound with 3 to 7 thin, elliptic leaflets with sharp points, to 3″ long.

Landscape Use Specimen, background, avenue, seaside, park, and large, open areas.

Flower Greenish, small, in racemes.

Flowering Season Spring.

Fruit Dark red capsule, ½″ long. Summer.

Soil & Moisture Grows best in dry, good soils.

pH Preference 5.5 to 8.5.

Salt Tolerance Excellent (1st line).

Freezes at about 28°F.

Rate of Growth Fast.

Propagation Seeds and cuttings. A limb of any size stuck into the ground will grow.

Culture Easy to grow.

Problems Branches are brittle and will break in high winds, but tree recovers rapidly. Caterpillars.

Scientific Name *Callistemon citrinus (C. lanceolatus)*

Common Name LEMON BOTTLEBRUSH

Family Myrtaceae

Approx. Height 25′ **Width** 10′

Native to Queensland.

Habit of Growth Small tree with erect or arching branches.

Description Leaves evergreen, simple, stiff, pubescent, lanceolate, to 3″ long. Crushed leaves have lemon-like odor.

Landscape Use Specimen, framing, border, and screen.

Flower Showy, bright red stamens on 2″ to 4″ spikes to 2½″ wide.

Flowering Season Spring and summer.

Fruit Small, woody capsules directly on stems.

Soil & Moisture Well-drained soil. Needs adequate moisture.

pH Preference 6.0 to 8.0.

Salt Tolerance Fair (2nd line).

Freezes at about 24°F.

Rate of Growth Moderate.

Propagation Seeds, soft wood cuttings under mist, and air layerings.

Culture Needs care until established. Prune to shape. Seed capsules are used in dried flower arrangements.

Problems Root rot disease. Scales. Nematodes.

Scientific Name *Callistemon viminalis* **Common Name** WEEPING BOTTLEBRUSH

Family Myrtaceae **Approx. Height** 20′ **Width** 20′

Native to Australia.

Habit of Growth Small tree with long and drooping branches.

Description Leaves evergreen, alternate, simple, slender to 4″ long. Pubescent when young.

Landscape Use Specimen, framing, patio, and avenue. Seasonal color.

Flower Deep red stamens in terminal spikes.

Flowering Season Early spring; some all year.

Fruit Small, woody capsules directly on stems.

Soil & Moisture Does best in moist to wet soils.

pH Preference 7.0 to 8.0.

Salt Tolerance Fair (2nd line).

Freezes at about 24°F.

Rate of Growth Fast.

Propagation Seeds, cuttings, and air layerings.

Culture Does best in full sun. Large plants are hard to move.

Problems Dieback and root rot diseases. Some insects. Nematodes.

Scientific Name *Calophyllum brasiliense (C. antillanum)* **Common Name** BRAZIL BEAUTY LEAF

Family Guttiferae **Approx. Height** 40′ **Width** 40′

Native to West Indies and tropical America.

Habit of Growth Medium large tree with rounded head.

Description Leaves evergreen, opposite, simple, glossy dark green, leathery, elliptic, to 6″ long and 2½″ wide. Numerous conspicuous veins at about right angles to midrib. New foliage reddish.

Landscape Use Framing, background, shade, and avenue.

Flower Cream, to ½″, in small racemes. Fragrant.

Flowering Season Spring.

Fruit Yellow-green, round drupe to 1″ with large seed.

Soil & Moisture Tolerant of most soils. Does not show mineral deficiencies.

pH Preference 6.0 to 8.0.

Salt Tolerance Fair (2nd line).

Freezes at about 25°F.

Rate of Growth Moderate.

Propagation Seeds. Crack seed coat and plant embryo.

Culture Easy to care for as it grows well in most soils when fertilized. Wind resistant.

Problems Scales. Fruit are a nuisance.

Scientific Name *Cananga odorata* **Common Name** YLANG-YLANG

Family Annonaceae **Approx. Height** 40′ **Width** 30′

Native to Malaya and S. E. Asia.

Habit of Growth Tree with long, slender, slightly drooping branches.

Description Leaves evergreen, alternate, simple, glossy above, oblongish, sharp pointed, to 10″ long and 3″ wide.

Landscape Use Specimen, background, border, and shade. Pruned to small tree.

Flower Greenish yellow, turning to deep yellow, 6 narrow petals, to 3″ long. Solitary or in small clusters. Very fragrant.

Flowering Season Most of the year.

Fruit Greenish becoming black, oval, fleshy, to 1″ long.

Soil & Moisture Well-drained, enriched soil.

pH Preference 6.0 to 8.0.

Salt Tolerance Poor (3rd line).

Freezes at about 32°F.

Rate of Growth Fast.

Propagation Seeds and air layerings.

Culture Little care needed once it is established. Dried flowers are used as a sachet and in perfumes.

Problems Caterpillars. Tree is very weak and is easily broken during high winds.

Scientific Name *Cassia fistula* **Common Name** GOLDEN-SHOWER

Family Leguminosae **Approx. Height** 30′ **Width** 25′

Native to India.

Habit of Growth Medium, upright tree with open top and slightly drooping branches.

Description Leaves briefly deciduous, even pinnately compound; leaflets opposite, 4 to 8 pairs, medium green, ovate or elliptic, to 8″ long and 2½″ wide.

Landscape Use Specimen, background, and avenue. Summer color.

Flower Golden yellow, 2″ wide, in 1′ long dangling racemes.

Flowering Season Summer.

Fruit Dark brown, cylindrical pod, 1″ thick and to 2′ long. Winter.

Soil & Moisture Tolerant of most soils. Prefers well-drained soil.

pH Preference 5.5 to 8.0.

Salt Tolerance Fair (2nd line).

Freezes at about 32°F. Will come back.

Rate of Growth Moderately fast.

Propagation Seeds.

Culture Prune to shape. Likes full sun. Black divisions in pod are used as a laxative.

Problems Mildew, leaf spot, and root rot diseases. Caterpillars. Sensitive to chemical sprays.

Scientific Name *Casuarina equisetifolia* **Common Name** AUSTRALIAN PINE BEEFWOOD

Family Casuarinaceae **Approx. Height** 80′ **Width** 35′

Native to Australia.

Habit of Growth Pine-like tree with single trunk and open, irregular crown.

Description Evergreen, grayish green, thin, needle-like, jointed branchlets, 4″ to 8″ long, with inconspicuous 6 or 7 scale-like leaves per whorl. Foliage is not dense.

Landscape Use Screen, hedge, roadside, seaside, and windbreak.

Flower Inconspicuous clusters. Female flower lateral; male flower terminal.

Flowering Season Spring.

Fruit Brown, small, cone-like, ¾″ long and ½″ wide.

Soil & Moisture Tolerant of most soils. Wet or dry soils.

pH Preference 6.0 to 8.0.

Salt Tolerance Excellent (1st line).

Freezes at about 26°F.

Rate of Growth Fast.

Propagation Seeds. They sprout and grow near parent tree. It has no suckers.

Culture Easy to grow.

Problems Mushroom root rot disease. Scales. Surface roots are a nuisance.

Scientific Name *Casuarina glauca*

Common Name BRAZILIAN-OAK
SUCKERING AUSTRALIAN PINE

Family Casuarinaceae

Approx. Height 70′ **Width** 30′

Native to Australia.

Habit of Growth Dense, pine-like tree. Pyramidal shape.

Description Evergreen, glossy green, thin, needle-like, jointed branchlets, 8″ to 10″ long and 1/32″ in diameter with inconspicuous 10 to 15 scale-like leaves per whorl.

Landscape Use Windbreak, sound and dust barrier.

Flower Inconspicuous. Male and female flowers on stems.

Flowering Season Spring.

Fruit Cone-like, oblong, to 1″ long. Seldom seen in Florida.

Soil & Moisture Stands wet soil if not brackish.

pH Preference 5.5 to 8.0.

Salt Tolerance Poor (3rd line). Will not stand salt spray.

Freezes at about 28°F.

Rate of Growth Fast.

Propagation Suckers. Best when grafted on C. *equisetifolia* seedlings.

Culture Easy to grow. C. *cunninghamiana* is a more hardy species.

Problems Suckers can become pests.

Scientific Name *Cecropia palmata* **Common Name** SNAKEWOOD TREE

Family Moraceae **Approx. Height** 50′ **Width** 40′

Native to West Indies, South and Central Americas.

Habit of Growth Large, open tree with slender, hollow trunk and branches.

Description Leaves evergreen, simple, palmately lobed, peltate, large, to 18″ in diameter. Silvery below, in clusters at tips of branches. Petiole 10″ to 18″. Milky sap.

Landscape Use Specimen, background, and border.

Flower Silvery green catkins in hanging clusters. Dioecious.

Flowering Season Late spring.

Fruit Compound, brownish, fleshy, spike-like, about 6″ long. Edible.

Soil & Moisture Prefers moist, enriched soil.

pH Preference 6.0 to 8.0.

Salt Tolerance Poor (3rd line).

Freezes at about 30°F.

Rate of Growth Very fast.

Propagation Seeds and air layerings.

Culture Once it is established it should be fertilized each year. Dried foliage is used in dry arrangements.

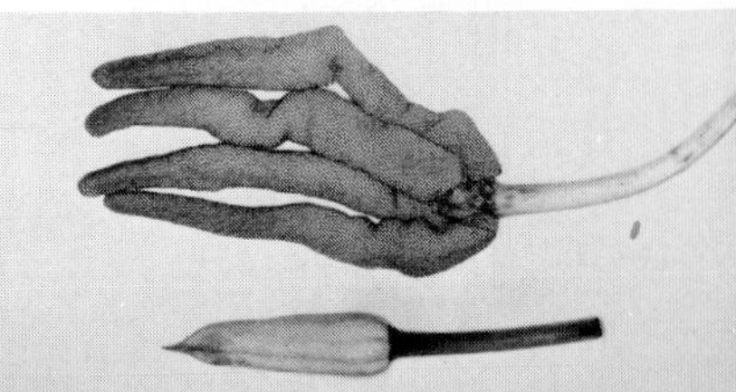

Problems Easily broken by winds. If male and female trees are in close proximity seedlings may be a nuisance.

Scientific Name *Celtis laevigata* **Common Name** HACKBERRY, SUGARBERRY MISSISSIPPI HACKBERRY

Family Ulmaceae **Approx. Height** 40′ **Width** 30′

Native to Florida, central and southeastern United States.

Habit of Growth Large, open tree with a straight trunk and broad head.

Description Leaves deciduous, simple, alternate, oblong-lanceolate with tapering tips, to 5″ long.

Landscape Use Background and naturalistic plantings.

Flower Inconspicuous. Greenish, axillary.

Flowering Season Late spring.

Fruit Orange-red to dark purple drupes about 1/4″ wide. Late summer. Birds eat them.

Soil & Moisture Tolerant of most soils. Needs adequate moisture.

pH Preference 6.0 to 8.0.

Salt Tolerance Poor (3rd line).

Freezes at about Hardy.

Rate of Growth Moderate.

Propagation Seeds.

Culture Little care required after tree becomes established.

Problems Leaf spot disease. Mites. Suckers.

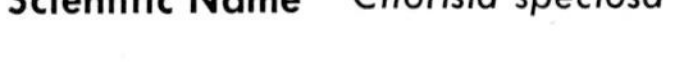

Scientific Name *Chorisia speciosa*

Common Name FLOSS-SILK TREE
SHOWY CHORISIA

Family Bombacaceae

Approx. Height 50′ **Width** 35′

Native to Brazil and Argentina.

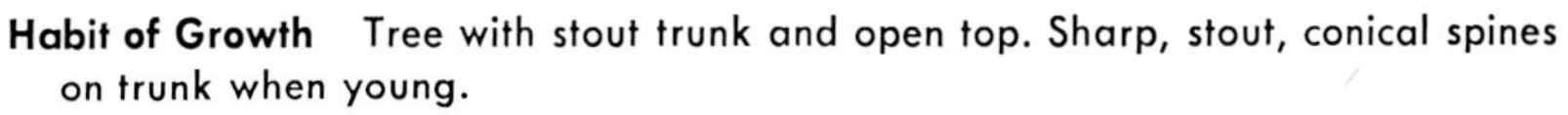

Habit of Growth Tree with stout trunk and open top. Sharp, stout, conical spines on trunk when young.

Description Leaves deciduous, alternate, palmately compound with 5 to 7 elliptic, finely toothed leaflets with tapering tips, to 5″ long.

Landscape Use Specimen and background. Fall color.

Flower Variable pink, 5 petals, to 8″ wide.

Flowering Season Fall.

Fruit Oblong capsule, 3″ to 6″ wide, containing fine floss and many seeds. Fruit seldom seen in Florida.

Soil & Moisture Tolerant of almost any soil.

pH Preference 6.0 to 8.0.

Salt Tolerance Poor (3rd line).

Freezes at about 30°F.

Rate of Growth Moderate.

Propagation Seeds, cuttings, and air layerings.

Culture Little care required after it is established. Needs full sun. Note: Another species C. *insignis* is the YELLOW-FLOWERED CHORISIA.

Problems Leaves and flowers are a nuisance.

Scientific Name *Chrysophyllum oliviforme* **Common Name** SATINLEAF

Family Sapotaceae **Approx. Height** 40′ **Width** 25′

Native to Florida and West Indies.

Habit of Growth Small to medium, upright tree with an open crown.

Description Leaves evergreen, alternate, simple, elliptic, pointed, 4″ to 6″ long. Bright green above and burnished copper below.

Landscape Use Specimen, framing, border, and patio.

Flower Small, whitish.

Flowering Season Fall.

Fruit Dark purple, smooth, berry-like, 3/4″ long. Winter to spring. Edible.

Soil & Moisture Tolerant of most soils. Prefers enriched, organic soil.

pH Preference 5.5 to 7.0.

Salt Tolerance Fair (2nd line).

Freezes at about 30°F.

Rate of Growth Moderate.

Propagation Seeds and air layerings.

Culture Fertile soil with mulch for best growth and appearance. *C. cainito,* STAR APPLE, is similar and has edible fruit.

Problems Leaf spot disease. Caterpillars.

Scientific Name *Cinnamomum camphora* **Common Name** CAMPHOR TREE

Family Lauraceae **Approx. Height** 50′ **Width** 40′

Native to China and Japan.

Habit of Growth Large, symmetrical, dense, spreading tree with low branches.

Description Leaves evergreen, alternate, simple, green and shiny, ovate-elliptic, pointed, to 5″ long. Leaves very aromatic (camphor) when crushed.

Landscape Use Shade and park. Avenue tree if lower limbs are removed.

Flower Yellow, small, in panicles.

Flowering Season Spring.

Fruit Black, shiny berry to ⅜″ wide. Birds eat berries.

Soil & Moisture Tolerant of most soils. Prefers good drainage.

pH Preference 5.5 to 6.5.

Salt Tolerance Poor (3rd line).

Freezes at about Hardy in Florida.

Rate of Growth Moderate to fast.

Propagation Seeds. Older trees difficult to transplant.

Culture Prune to shape. Shows manganese deficiency in alkaline soils.

Problems Dieback, root rot, and leaf spot diseases. Mites. Grass does not grow under this tree because of its heavy shade. Berries are a nuisance.

Scientific Name *Citrofortunella mitis (Citrus mitis)*

Common Name CALAMONDIN

Family Rutaceae

Approx. Height 20′ **Width** 10′

Native to Philippines.

Habit of Growth Small, upright, dense tree.

Description Leaves evergreen, alternate, compound but simple in appearance, glossy, dark green, elliptic, pointed, to 3″ long.

Landscape Use Specimen and framing. Flower and fruit color.

Flower Small, white, ½″ long. Fragrant.

Flowering Season Spring and periodically.

Fruit Orange-yellow, miniature tangerine, 1½″ in diameter. Very acid. Everbearing.

Soil & Moisture Well-drained, enriched soil.

pH Preference 5.5 to 6.5.

Salt Tolerance Fair (2nd line).

Freezes at about 22°F.

Rate of Growth Moderate.

Propagation Seeds, cuttings, buddings, and air layerings.

Culture Same as for any citrus tree. Fruit used as a lime substitute.

Problems Scales and whiteflies. Spider mites and rust mites.

Scientific Name *Clusia rosea*

Common Name MONKEY APPLE
PITCH APPLE

Family Guttiferae

Approx. Height 30′ **Width** 20′

Native to Bahamas, West Indies, and tropical America.

Habit of Growth Small tree with dense crown and wide-spreading, horizontal, irregular branches. Occasional aerial roots.

Description Leaves evergreen, opposite, simple, thick with thick midvein, obovate, to 8″ long and 4″ wide. Glossy above and dull below.

Landscape Use Specimen, framing, and background. Can be an espalier specimen. Used as a tall shrub. Seaside.

Flower Showy, pink or white, 3″ across.

Flowering Season Summer and early fall.

Fruit Greenish white, globose capsule, to 3″ wide.

Soil & Moisture Tolerant of most soils.

pH Preference 5.5 to 7.5.

Salt Tolerance Excellent (1st line).

Freezes at about 32°F.

Rate of Growth Moderate.

Propagation Seeds, cuttings, and air layerings.

Culture Needs little care after it is established. Wind resistant. Note: There is a clone with variegated leaves.

Problems Free of serious pests and problems. Scales. May have surface roots.

Scientific Name *Coccoloba diversifolia* **Common Name** PIGEON PLUM
DOVE PLUM

Family Polygonaceae **Approx. Height** 40′ **Width** 25′

Native to South Florida, Bahamas, and West Indies.

Habit of Growth Tree with straight trunk, light gray bark, and dense, rounded crown.

Description Leaves evergreen, alternate, simple, bright green, leathery, ovate, to 4″ long. Base of petiole wraps around stem.

Landscape Use Specimen and framing. Good for planting in dooryards and parkways. Seaside.

Flower Whitish, in slender racemes 3″ to 6″ long.

Flowering Season Spring.

Fruit Dark purple to ½″ across. Edible. Winter.

Soil & Moisture Dry sandy soils.

pH Preference 6.5 to 8.0.

Salt Tolerance Excellent (1st line).

Freezes at about 32°F.

Rate of Growth Moderate to slow.

Propagation Seeds, ripe wood cuttings, and air layerings.

Culture Prune to shape.

Problems Few. Twig borers.

Scientific Name *Coccoloba uvifera* **Common Name** SEA GRAPE

Family Polygonaceae **Approx. Height** 25′ **Width** 25′

Native to South Florida, Bahamas, West Indies, and tropical America.

Habit of Growth Shrubby, small tree with a spreading crown and stout branches.

Description Leaves evergreen, alternate, simple, green with red veins, thick, leathery, nearly circular, to 8″ across. Young leaves bronze in color. Old leaves turn reddish before they fall in late winter.

Landscape Use Background, framing, tropical effect, and seaside.

Flower Small, white, in racemes, to 12″ long.

Flowering Season May.

Fruit Green turning purple, grape-like, ¾″ in diameter. Edible. September to October.

Soil & Moisture Enriched, sandy soil.

pH Preference 6.0 to 8.0.

Salt Tolerance Excellent (1st line).

Freezes at about 30°F. Leaves bronzed by cold.

Rate of Growth Moderate.

Propagation Seeds, cuttings, and air layerings.

Culture Can be trimmed as a hedge or espaliered. Prune to shape. Fruit eaten fresh or in jelly. A variegated cultivar is available.

Problems Leaf spot disease. Scales and a tip borer.

Scientific Name *Conocarpus erectus* **Common Name** BUTTONWOOD

Family Combretaceae **Approx. Height** 60′ **Width** 30′

Native to South Florida, Bahamas, West Indies, and tropical America.

Habit of Growth Tree with narrow top. Trunk sometimes twisted or horizontal.

Description Leaves evergreen, alternate, simple, grayish green, slender, to 4″ long.

Landscape Use Specimen, framing, screen, and seaside.

Flower White, tiny, button-like, in terminal panicles.

Flowering Season All year.

Fruit Dark, cone-like, ½″ across.

Soil & Moisture Grows in brackish, wet, or sandy soils.

pH Preference 5.5 to 7.5.

Salt Tolerance Excellent (1st line).

Freezes at about 28°F.

Rate of Growth Moderate.

Propagation Seeds, cuttings, and air layerings.

Culture Easy to grow. Note: Variety 'sericea', SILVER BUTTONWOOD, pictured above, has silver-gray foliage.

Problems Leaf diseases. Scales and sooty mold.

LANDSCAPE PLAN SHOWING USE OF TREES

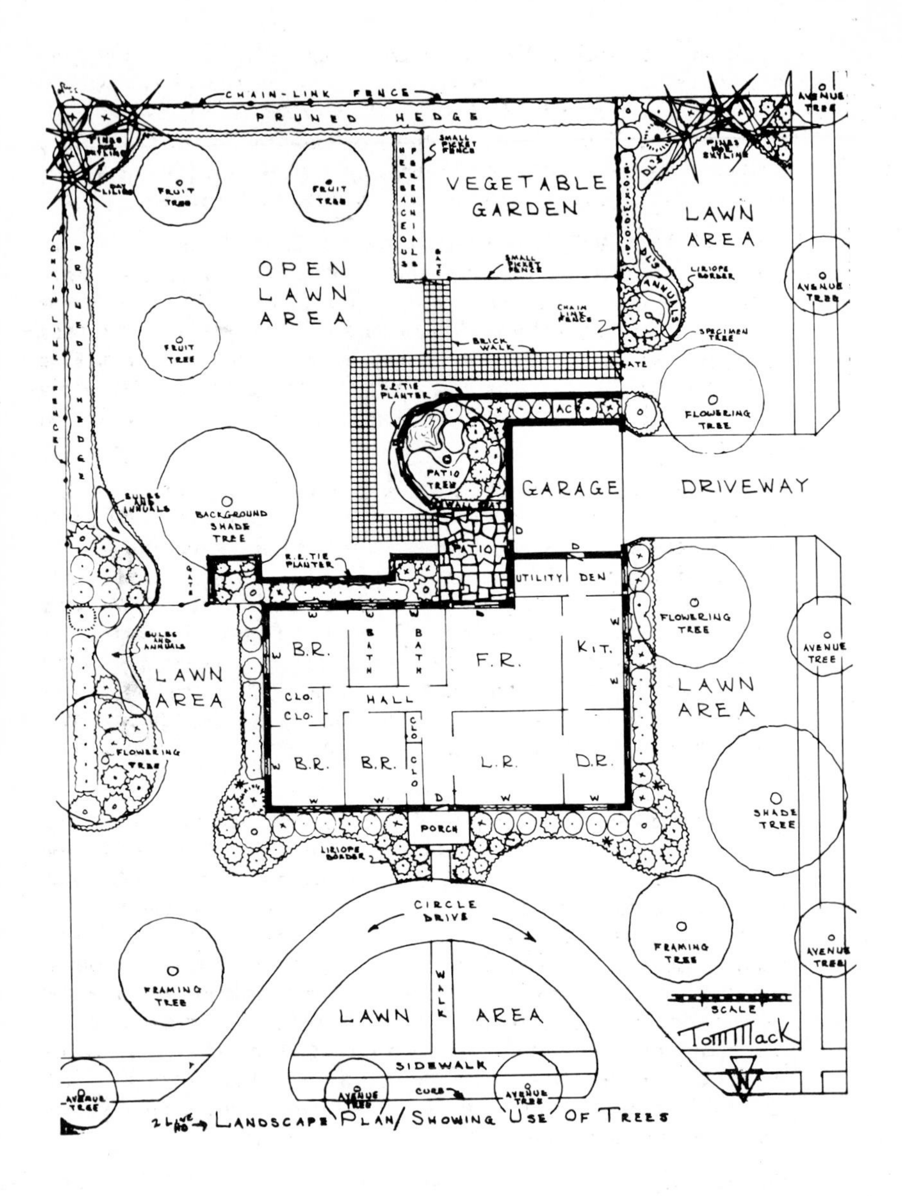

TREES IN THE LANDSCAPE

by Professor Thomas B. Mack

One of the first and perhaps the most important thing that you will do in developing a landscape plan is to decide on the trees that you will use. Trees add dimension, scale, and profile to the garden composition and, therefore, are an indispensable element in the landscape. Any successful landscape development must properly utilize trees for shade, framing, screening, background, skyline, and points of interest.

TREES ARE PERMANENT. It is easy enough to move plants around, change the design of walks and paths, hedges, etc., when they have been located in the wrong places. It is difficult though to move a tree after it is planted and established. As one author has put it, "Think ten times before you plant a tree". Since it takes many years for a tree to do the complete job that is required of it in the landscape, it is extremely important to make sure that you have properly planned for it in the composition.

It is basic to start with trees as the first part of landscape planning. Trees often exist naturally on the property and decisions must be made concerning these. However, most trees are planted as young specimens, and you need to understand something about the growth of trees and their care as a part of making the selection of a tree to plant. You need to know the type of soil suitable for the tree. Will the tree grow in a sandy, well-drained soil? Can the tree exist near salt water or tolerate salt spray? What is the proper pH that is best for the tree? What are the diseases and insects that might be problems with the selected tree? These are some of the questions that the information in this book will answer.

Trees have certain jobs to do in the landscape. You need to know the characteristics of the selected tree to understand its proper use in the design. Trees that provide a setting for the house are important. When we plant trees so that we view the house through them, we refer to this as framing. Trees play an important role in providing privacy. Using trees for this purpose is often referred to as screening. When trees are used as specimens, they can be a point of interest. This is especially true when a tree is in bloom. Trees seen over the roof line of the house are often called background trees, and these trees provide a break in the skyline to hold the eye on the scene. It is important to know just what jobs your tree can do in your design. Information is provided in the **Landscape Use** of trees in this book in order that you can understand this.

Through careful study and selection, you can easily have color provided by trees almost every day of the year. A little time spent in planning for tree plantings will not only provide a beautiful landscape picture but will also impart a feeling of permanence and stability to the neighborhood. The proper use of trees will enhance the beauty of the home — increase the value of properties — make for a more pleasant community — and even make the world a better place in which to live.

Scientific Name *Cordia sebestena* **Common Name** GEIGER TREE

Family Ehretiaceae (Boraginaceae) **Approx. Height** 25′ **Width** 15′

Native to South Florida, Bahamas, West Indies, and South America.

Habit of Growth Small tree with slender trunk and dense, rounded top.

Description Leaves evergreen, alternate, simple, ovate, to 8″ long. Leaves rough-hairy above, smooth and lighter color below.

Landscape Use Specimen, framing, border, patio, and seaside.

Flower Brilliant orange-red, salverform, with 6 petals, 1½″ across, in flat-topped, terminal clusters.

Flowering Season Best in June and July. Occasionally all year.

Fruit White, smooth, oval drupe about 1″ long.

Soil & Moisture Tolerant of alkaline and brackish soils.

pH Preference 5.5 to 8.5.

Salt Tolerance Excellent (1st line).

Freezes at about 32°F.

Rate of Growth Moderate to slow.

Propagation Seeds and air layerings. Transplants easily.

Culture Easy to grow with little care.

Problems Leaf spot and rust diseases. Scales. Mites. Beetles eat leaves.

Scientific Name *Cornus florida* **Common Name** FLOWERING DOGWOOD

Family Cornaceae **Approx. Height** 30′ **Width** 20′

Native to North America.

Habit of Growth Small, spreading tree.

Description Leaves deciduous, opposite, simple, ovate, 2″ to 6″ long. Dark green above and pale below, turning red before they fall.

Landscape Use Specimen, framing, border, and avenue.

Flower Showy parts are 4 white, petal-like bracts, 3″ to 4″ across.

Flowering Season Spring.

Fruit Red drupes, ½″ long, in clusters. Fall. Birds eat them.

Soil & Moisture Well-drained, enriched soil.

pH Preference 5.0 to 6.0.

Salt Tolerance Poor (3rd line).

Freezes at about Hardy.

Rate of Growth Moderate.

Propagation Seeds, cuttings, graftings, and air layerings.

Culture Likes some shade. Best in north and north central Florida. Grows poorly in eastern coastal areas of central and south Florida.

Problems Root rot and leaf spot diseases. Borers and thrips.

Scientific Name *Cupaniopsis anacardioides* **Common Name** CARROTWOOD

Family Sapindaceae **Approx. Height** 25′ **Width** 25′

Native to Australia.

Habit of Growth Small, umbrella-shaped tree.

Description Leaves evergreen, alternate, pinnately compound, to 12″ long. Leaflets alternate, dark green, leathery, oblongish, to 4″ long.

Landscape Use Specimen, framing, and patio.

Flower Inconspicuous. Greenish white.

Flowering Season Winter.

Fruit 3-lobed capsule with orange-red flesh and black seeds. June.

Soil & Moisture Well-drained, enriched soil.

pH Preference 6.0 to 8.0.

Salt Tolerance Fair (2nd line).

Freezes at about 25°F.

Rate of Growth Moderate.

Propagation Seeds and air layerings. Grows easily from seeds which will germinate in two weeks.

Culture Will grow in pumped in fill. Responds to fertilizer and water. Easy to move.

Problems Leaf spot diseases. Scales and aphids. Mites. Nematodes. Wind scorch. Seedlings can become a nuisance.

Scientific Name *Dalbergia sissoo*

Common Name SISSOO TREE
INDIAN ROSEWOOD

Family Leguminosae

Approx. Height 60′ **Width** 45′

Native to India.

Habit of Growth Upright tree forming an open top. Twigs green to gray.

Description Leaves semi-evergreen, pinnately compound with 3 to 5 alternate, light green, roundish leaflets with pointed tips, on a zigzag rachis, to 4″ long.

Landscape Use Specimen, framing, background, and avenue.

Flower Yellowish or white, small, pea-shaped, in clusters. Fragrant.

Flowering Season Summer.

Fruit Brown, flat, slender pod to 4″ long.

Soil & Moisture Most soils, dry to moist.

pH Preference 5.5 to 7.0.

Salt Tolerance Fair (2nd line).

Freezes at about 20°F.

Rate of Growth Fast.

Propagation Seeds, cuttings, and air layerings.

Culture Easy to grow. Very wind tolerant.

Problems Few. Leaf spot disease. Will sucker from damaged roots.

Scientific Name *Delonix regia* **Common Name** ROYAL POINCIANA

Family Leguminosae **Approx. Height** 40′ **Width** 50′

Native to Madagascar.

Habit of Growth Graceful tree with stiff, wide-spreading branches.

Description Leaves deciduous, even-bipinnately compound, fern-like, to 2′ long, with numerous pairs of medium green, tiny, oval leaflets about ½″ long.

Landscape Use Avenue, park, and other large, open areas. Seasonal color.

Flower Showy, variable, orange to red with one striped petal, to 4″ across, in large clusters.

Flowering Season April to July.

Fruit Dark brown, flat, woody pod 2″ wide to 2′ long.

Soil & Moisture Most well-drained soils. Will not take wet soils.

pH Preference 5.5 to 7.5.

Salt Tolerance Fair (2nd line).

Freezes at about 32°F.

Rate of Growth Fast.

Propagation Seeds.

Culture Low maintenance.

Problems Dieback and root rot diseases. Aggressive surface roots. Pods are a nuisance. Slow coming into flower.

Scientific Name *Enterolobium cyclocarpum* **Common Name** EAR TREE

Family Leguminosae **Approx. Height** 50+′ **Width** 55+′

Native to West Indies and tropical America.

Habit of Growth Huge, wide-spreading tree with large trunk.

Description Leaves deciduous, even-bipinnately compound, fern-like, to about 11″ long, with many pairs of light green, tiny, narrow, pointed leaflets to ½″ long.

Landscape Use Park and other large, open areas.

Flower Whitish, fluffy, in small, globose, ½″ clusters.

Flowering Season Spring to early summer.

Fruit Shining, dark brown, ear-shaped pod to 4″ long.

Soil & Moisture Most soils with fair drainage.

pH Preference 5.5 to 7.5.

Salt Tolerance Poor (3rd line).

Freezes at about 25°F.

Rate of Growth Fast.

Propagation Seeds, suckers, and cuttings.

Culture Little care is needed. Lawn will grow under it.

Problems Aggressive surface roots. Too large for city lots.

Scientific Name *Eucalyptus camaldulensis* **Common Name** RED GUM

Family Myrtaceae **Approx. Height** 80′ **Width** 30′

Native to Australia.

Habit of Growth Tall tree with a large trunk, gray, deciduous bark, slender branches and twigs, and an open crown.

Description Leaves evergreen, simple, grayish green, slender, lanceolate, curving toward the tip, to 8″ long.

Landscape Use Specimen, background, park, and windbreak.

Flower Inconspicuous. White, on new growth.

Flowering Season Spring.

Fruit Small, globular, 1/4″ long, in clusters.

Soil & Moisture Wide range of soils.

pH Preference 5.5 to 7.0.

Salt Tolerance Poor (3rd line).

Freezes at about 20°F.

Rate of Growth Fast.

Propagation Seeds.

Culture Top periodically to keep down height. Note: Most widespread species in Australia.

Problems Root rot, crown gall, and leaf spot diseases. Scales. Mites. Too large for most homes. Not a good shade tree.

Scientific Name *Eucalyptus cinerea* **Common Name** SILVER-DOLLAR EUCALYPTUS

Family Myrtaceae **Approx. Height** 15′-30′ **Width** 10′

Native to Australia.

Habit of Growth Small, open tree with irregular crown.

Description Leaves evergreen, opposite, simple, spiral-like, silvery, bluish gray, small, oval to heart-shaped with no petioles.

Landscape Use Specimen and patio.

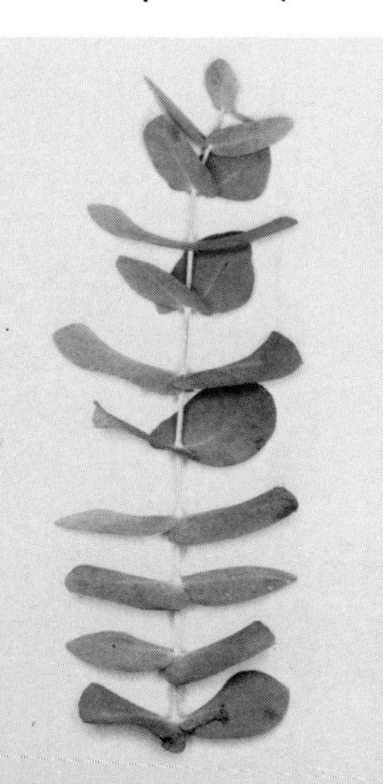

Flower Inconspicuous. Small, white, in clusters.

Flowering Season Summer.

Fruit Small, roundish capsule ¼″ across.

Soil & Moisture Tolerant of most soils.

pH Preference 5.5 to 7.5.

Salt Tolerance Fair (2nd line).

Freezes at about 20°F. Fairly hardy.

Rate of Growth Moderate.

Propagation Seeds.

Culture Leaves must be protected from mites and diseases. Foliage used by florists.

Problems Fungus disease of leaves. Dieback and root rot diseases. Mites.

Scientific Name *Ficus altissima* **Common Name** LOFTY FIG
FALSE BANYAN

Family Moraceae **Approx. Height** 70′ **Width** 150′

Native to India.

Habit of Growth Large, spreading tree with rounded crown.

Description Leaves evergreen, alternate, simple, glossy above, thick, broad-oval, to 8″ long. Milky sap. Usually has aerial roots.

Landscape Use Avenue, park, and other large, open areas.

Flower A fig.

Flowering Season April to May.

Fruit Red, small, ovoid fig to ¾″ across.

Soil & Moisture Tolerant of most soils.

pH Preference 6.0 to 7.5.

Salt Tolerance Fair (2nd line).

Freezes at about 30°F.

Rate of Growth Very fast.

Propagation Cuttings and air layerings.

Culture Easily grown.

Problems In alkaline soils it may be chlorotic. Underground roots can damage walks, walls, etc. Too large for average lot.

Scientific Name *Ficus aurea* **Common Name** FLORIDA STRANGLER FIG

Family Moraceae **Approx. Height** 60′ **Width** 60′

Native to South Florida, Bahamas, and West Indies.

Habit of Growth Stocky tree with spreading branches.

Description Leaves semi-deciduous, alternate, simple, shining, dark green, oval with pointed tips, to 4″ long. Milky sap. Aerial roots.

Landscape Use Park and other large, open areas.

Flower A fig.

Flowering Season All year. Heavy in late spring and early summer.

Fruit Yellow to red, small, round, stemless fig to about ½″ across. Edible.

Soil & Moisture Any type soil.

pH Preference 5.5 to 7.0.

Salt Tolerance Fair (2nd line).

Freezes at about 30°F.

Rate of Growth Fast.

Propagation Seeds.

Culture A strangler fig. It begins as a seed germinating on a host tree. Then it produces aerial roots and gradually strangles its host.

Problems Scales and aphids. Mites. Too large for average lot.

Scientific Name *Ficus benjamina*

Common Name WEEPING FIG
BENJAMIN FIG

Family Moraceae

Approx. Height 50′ **Width** 80′

Native to India and Malaya.

Habit of Growth Symmetrical tree with a short, stout trunk, spreading, drooping branches, and a dense crown.

Description Leaves evergreen, alternate, simple, shining, oval with long tapering tips, to 5″ long. Milky sap. Aerial roots on old trees.

Landscape Use Tall hedge, avenue, pot or urn, park, and large, open areas.

Flower A fig.

Flowering Season Summer.

Fruit Red, small, round fig ⅓″ across. Borne in pairs.

Soil & Moisture Tolerant of a wide range of soils.

pH Preference 5.5 to 7.0.

Salt Tolerance Fair (2nd line).

Freezes at about 28 °F.

Rate of Growth Fast.

Propagation Cuttings and air layerings.

Culture Occasional top pruning. Resistant to foliar thrips.

Problems Scales. Aggressive surface roots. Too large for average lot.

Scientific Name *Ficus elastica*

Common Name RUBBER PLANT
INDIA RUBBER TREE

Family Moraceae

Approx. Height 100′ **Width** 100′

Native to India to Malaya.

Habit of Growth Large, spreading tree with a short trunk.

Description Leaves evergreen, alternate, simple, glossy, thick, broad-oval with pointed tips, to 12″ long. Milky sap. Aerial roots.

Landscape Use Park and other large, open areas. Pot or urn and indoor planters.

Flower A fig.

Flowering Season Summer.

Fruit Yellowish fig to ½″ long. Borne in pairs.

Soil & Moisture Tolerant of most soils.

pH Preference 6.0 to 7.5.

Salt Tolerance Fair (2nd line).

Freezes at about 30°F.

Rate of Growth Fast.

Propagation Cuttings and air layerings.

Culture No special care required. Some cultivars are more popular than the species, such as two variegated forms: a purple leaved form and one with a coppery-red new growth.

Problems Scales. Aggressive surface roots. Too large for average lot.

Scientific Name *Ficus lyrata*
(F. pandurata)

Common Name FIDDLE-LEAF FIG

Family Moraceae

Approx. Height 40′ **Width** 50′

Native to Tropical Africa.

Habit of Growth Upright tree with spreading branches.

Description Leaves evergreen, alternate, simple, leathery, fiddle-shaped 10″ to 15″ long and 6″ to 8″ wide. Dark green above and lighter below. Milky sap.

Landscape Use Specimen, patio, pot or urn, and indoor planters.

Flower A fig.

Flowering Season Summer.

Fruit Green fig with white dots, to 2″ across. Borne in pairs.

Soil & Moisture Tolerant of most soils.

pH Preference 5.5 to 7.0.

Salt Tolerance Poor (3rd line).

Freezes at about 32°F.

Rate of Growth Moderate.

Propagation Cuttings and air layerings.

Culture Easy to grow. Prune to reduce height.

Problems Leaf disease. Scales. Can be injured by strong winds. Fruit and leaves are a nuisance. Too large for average lot.

Scientific Name *Ficus retusa*

Common Name INDIAN LAUREL

Family Moraceae

Approx. Height 90′ **Width** 90′

Native to India and Malaya.

Habit of Growth Upright, large tree with short, thick trunk, spreading branches and a dense crown.

Description Leaves evergreen, alternate, simple, dark glossy green, oval with pointed tips, to 4″ long. Milky sap. Few aerial roots.

Landscape Use Hedge, avenue, park, and other large, open areas. Pot or urn and indoor planters.

Flower A fig.

Flowering Season Spring to summer.

Fruit Purple fig, ⅓″ across. Borne in pairs.

Soil & Moisture Likes moist soil but tolerant.

pH Preference 5.5 to 7.0.

Salt Tolerance Fair (2nd line).

Freezes at about 27°F.

Rate of Growth Fast.

Propagation Cuttings and air layerings.

Culture Easy to grow.

Problems Leaf spot disease. Thrips curl leaves. Underground roots can damage walks, walls, etc. Too large for average lot.

Scientific Name *Gordonia lasianthus* **Common Name** LOBLOLLY BAY

Family Theaceae **Approx. Height** 60′ **Width** 30′

Native to Virginia to Florida to Mississippi.

Habit of Growth Large, upright tree.

Description Leaves evergreen, alternate, simple, shining, dark green above, smooth, oval and shallow toothed, to 6″ long.

Landscape Use Specimen, shade, and avenue.

Flower Showy, white with golden stamens, about 2½″ across. Fragrant.

Flowering Season Early spring; some all year.

Fruit Woody capsule, egg-shaped and slightly pointed, to ¾″ long.

Soil & Moisture Enriched, moist soil preferred.

pH Preference 4.5 to 7.5.

Salt Tolerance Fair (2nd line).

Freezes at about Hardy.

Rate of Growth Moderate.

Propagation Seeds and greenwood cuttings.

Culture Native tree. Easy to grow.

Problems Leaf spot disease. Aphids and borers.

Scientific Name *Grevillea robusta* **Common Name** SILK OAK

Family Proteaceae **Approx. Height** 80′ **Width** 40′

Native to Australia.

Habit of Growth Pyramidal-shaped tree with straight, tall trunk.

Description Leaves evergreen, alternate, compound, deeply cut, fern-like, leathery and stiff, 6″ to 12″ long. Leaflets lanceolate, dark green above and silvery below.

Landscape Use Specimen, framing, background, skyline, and avenue.

Flower Yellow-orange, odd-shaped spikes in clusters on old twigs, to 5″ long.

Flowering Season April and May.

Fruit Leathery follicle about ¾″ long.

Soil & Moisture Most well-drained soils.

pH Preference 5.5 to 7.5.

Salt Tolerance Fair (2nd line).

Freezes at about 27°F. when young.

Rate of Growth Fast.

Propagation Seeds.

Culture It will stand considerable drought. RED SILK OAK, *G. banksii,* is a small, red flowered tree.

Problems Mushroom foot rot disease. Sapsuckers attack trunk. Gumming. Damaged by hurricanes. Old trees are brittle and look ragged. Surface roots and leaves are a problem in lawns. Too large for small lot.

Scientific Name *Hibiscus tiliaceus*

Common Name MAHOE
SEA HIBISCUS

Family Malvaceae

Approx. Height 40′ **Width** 50′

Native to South Florida, Bahamas, and world tropics.

Habit of Growth Tree with light gray bark and dense, rounded top. Spreading branches touch ground and may root.

Description Leaves evergreen, alternate, simple, dark green, coarse, somewhat heart-shaped, 3″ to 8″ wide or long.

Landscape Use Shade, highways, park, and seaside.

Flower Hibiscus-like to 4″ across. Opens yellow with or without maroon eye and turns dark rose by evening.

Flowering Season Spring and summer.

Fruit Ovoid, pointed, tomentose, leathery capsule, ¾″ long.

Soil & Moisture Stands poor, dry, sandy soils and brackish water.

pH Preference 5.5 to 8.0.

Salt Tolerance Excellent (1st line).

Freezes at about 32°F.

Rate of Growth Fast.

Propagation Seeds and cuttings.

Culture Grows well in pumped in soil.

Problems Scales. Deficiencies of essential elements. Leaves and flowers are a nuisance. Too large for small lot.

Scientific Name *Ilex cassine* **Common Name** DAHOON HOLLY

Family Aquifoliaceae **Approx. Height** 40′ **Width** 20′

Native to Virginia to Texas to Florida Keys and Bahamas.

Habit of Growth Erect, compact tree with narrow, close head.

Description Leaves evergreen, alternate, simple, medium green, leathery, smooth, obovate to elliptic, to about 4″ long. Few teeth near tips.

Landscape Use Specimen, framing, tall hedge, shade tree near house and avenue. Colorful berries.

Flower Small, white. Male and female flowers on different plants.

Flowering Season Spring.

Fruit Red, round drupes to ⅜″ wide. Winter. Birds eat them.

Soil & Moisture Will grow on sandy or wet soil.

pH Preference 4.5 to 7.0.

Salt Tolerance Fair (2nd line).

Freezes at about Hardy.

Rate of Growth Slow.

Propagation Cuttings and graftings.

Culture Little care once established.

Problems Leaf diseases. Scales, leaf miners, and spittle bugs. Only female tree produces berries and needs a male tree nearby.

Scientific Name *Ilex opaca* **Common Name** AMERICAN HOLLY

Family Aquifoliaceae **Approx. Height** 45′ **Width** 20′

Native to Massachusetts to Florida and west to Missouri and Texas.

Habit of Growth Upright, pyramidal tree with dense head.

Description Leaves evergreen, alternate, simple, dull green, leathery, obovate to elliptic with spiny margins, 2″ to 4″ long.

Landscape Use Specimen, patio, and avenue.

Flower Small, creamy. Male and female flowers on different plants.

Flowering Season Midsummer.

Fruit Red, round drupes usually ¼″ across. Winter. Birds eat them.

Soil & Moisture Enriched, well-drained soil.

pH Preference 4.5 to 7.0.

Salt Tolerance Fair (2nd line).

Freezes at about Hardy.

Rate of Growth Slow.

Propagation Cuttings and graftings.

Culture Should be mulched to retain moisture. Many named clones. 'East Palatka' and 'Savannah' are recommended for south Florida.

Problems Scales, leaf miners, and spittle bugs. Only female tree produces berries and needs a male tree nearby.

Scientific Name *Jacaranda mimosifolia* **Common Name** JACARANDA

Family Bignoniaceae **Approx. Height** *50′* **Width** *45′*

Native to Brazil, N.W. Argentina.

Habit of Growth Large, tall, asymmetrical tree with a spreading, open top.

Description Leaves deciduous, opposite, bipinnately compound, fern-like, to about 15″ long. Leaflets medium green, pointed, to ½″ long.

Landscape Use Specimen, framing, and skyline. Good for summer shade.

Flower Violet-blue, trumpet-shaped, to 2″ long, in large, showy panicles. Odd fragrance.

Flowering Season April to June.

Fruit Brown, roundish, flat, woody capsule about 2″ across.

Soil & Moisture Well-drained soil.

pH Preference 5.5 to 7.0.

Salt Tolerance Poor (3rd line).

Freezes at about 26°F. Will come back.

Rate of Growth Moderate.

Propagation Seeds and cuttings of half-ripened wood. Grafted trees flower sooner.

Culture Requires little care after it is established. Prune when small to shape tree. Note: A white flowering cultivar is available.

Problems Root rot disease. Nematodes. Brittle, do not plant near a house.

Scientific Name *Juniperus silicicola* **Common Name** SOUTHERN RED CEDAR

Family Cupressaceae **Approx. Height** 50′ **Width** 30′

Native to S.E. United States.

Habit of Growth Cone-shaped tree when young. It becomes flat-topped with age.

Description Leaves evergreen, dark green, small, scale-like. Fragrant.

Landscape Use Specimen, framing, background, screen, pot or urn, seaside, and windbreak. Christmas tree.

Flower Inconspicuous. Dioecious.

Flowering Season Spring.

Fruit Dark blue, pea-sized, fleshy cones. Birds eat them.

Soil & Moisture Well-drained, sandy soils.

pH Preference 5.5 to 7.5.

Salt Tolerance Fair (2nd line).

Freezes at about Hardy.

Rate of Growth Moderate.

Propagation Seeds and cuttings.

Culture Little care is needed. Does best in full sun.

Problems Twig blight and dieback diseases. Bagworms. Mites.

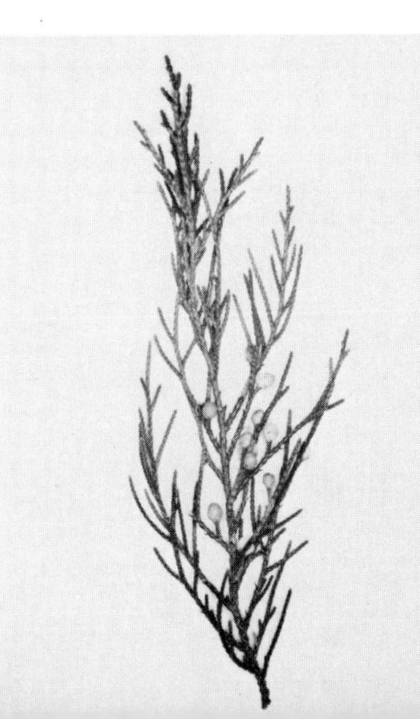

Scientific Name *Koelreuteria elegans (K. formosana)*

Common Name GOLDEN-RAIN TREE

Family Sapindaceae

Approx. Height 40′ **Width** 30′

Native to Formosa.

Habit of Growth A somewhat open tree with irregular, spreading branches.

Description Leaves deciduous, alternate, bipinnately compound, to 18″ long. Leaflets shallowly toothed, pointed, to 3″ long.

Landscape Use Specimen and shade. For fall color.

Flower Yellow, small, in terminal panicles.

Flowering Season September to November.

Fruit Showy, pink to rose, papery bracts cover capsules containing three black seeds.

Soil & Moisture Tolerant of most soils. Grows on most well-drained soils.

pH Preference 6.0 to 8.0.

Salt Tolerance Poor (3rd line).

Freezes at about Hardy.

Rate of Growth Moderate to fast.

Propagation Seeds. Seedlings usually found growing under trees.

Culture Easy to grow. Wind resistant.

Problems Mushroom root rot and leaf spot diseases. Scales. Flowers and fruit are a nuisance. Seedlings are a problem in flower beds.

Scientific Name *Lagerstroemia indica* **Common Name** CRAPE MYRTLE

Family Lythraceae **Approx. Height** 25′ **Width** 15′

Native to China.

Habit of Growth Small, upright tree or shrub often with several trunks. Smooth, brown, mottled bark.

Description Leaves deciduous, alternate, simple, light green, to 3″ long.

Landscape Use Specimen, framing, background, and border.

Flower Purple, red, pink, or white with fringed petals in large, showy panicles.

Flowering Season May to August.

Fruit Brown, rounded, woody capsule about ½″ across.

Soil & Moisture Tolerant of many different soils.

pH Preference 5.0 to 7.0.

Salt Tolerance Fair (2nd line).

Freezes at about Hardy.

Rate of Growth Moderate.

Propagation Seeds and cuttings.

Culture Prune when dormant for better bloom and shape. No special care required. Dwarf cultivars are available.

Problems Powdery mildew disease. Aphids. Leaves often show mottling of manganese deficiency.

Scientific Name *Lagerstroemia speciosa* **Common Name** QUEEN'S CRAPE MYRTLE

Family Lythraceae **Approx. Height** 40′ **Width** 30′

Native to India and East Indies to Australia.

Habit of Growth Tree with broad, rounded top.

Description Leaves deciduous, alternate, simple, dark green, leathery, oblong to ovate tapering to a point, to 12″ long. Leaves turn red in fall.

Landscape Use Specimen, framing, and avenue. For spectacular bloom.

Flower Pink to lavender with fringed petals, to 3″ across, in large, showy terminal panicles.

Flowering Season June to August.

Fruit Roundish, woody capsule to 1″ across, turns black.

Soil & Moisture Tolerant of a wide range of soils.

pH Preference 5.5 to 7.0.

Salt Tolerance Fair (2nd line).

Freezes at about 32°F.

Rate of Growth Slow to moderate.

Propagation Seeds, cuttings, and root shoots.

Culture Adapted to south Florida. Likes full sun or partial shade.

Problems Powdery mildew disease. Scales.

Scientific Name *Liquidambar styraciflua* **Common Name** SWEET GUM

Family Hamamelidaceae **Approx. Height** 80′ **Width** 40′

Native to Connecticut to Florida and South America.

Habit of Growth Vigorous, pyramidal-shaped when young.

Description Leaves deciduous, alternate, simple, palmate, usually 5-lobed, toothed, about 4″ long and wide. Leaves turn red and yellow in late fall. Some twigs have corky wings.

Landscape Use Specimen, background, shade, and avenue.

Flower Inconspicuous. Greenish yellow clusters.

Flowering Season Early spring.

Fruit Brown, spiny, globe about 1″ across.

Soil & Moisture Tolerant of most soils. Best on moist soil rich in humus.

pH Preference 5.5 to 6.5.

Salt Tolerance Fair (2nd line).

Freezes at about Hardy.

Rate of Growth Fast.

Propagation Seeds.

Culture Do not disturb roots. Transplant when dormant. *L. formosana* is better suited for south Florida.

Problems Leaf spot disease. Borers. Leaves and fruit are a nuisance.

Scientific Name *Lysiloma bahamensis* **Common Name** WILD TAMARIND

Family Leguminosae **Approx. Height** 60′ **Width** 40′

Native to South Florida, Bahamas, and West Indies.

Habit of Growth Erect tree with slender trunk and spreading and drooping branches.

Description Leaves deciduous, alternate, bipinnately compound, fern-like, with oblong leaflets to ½″ long, pale below.

Landscape Use Background, shade, park, and seaside.

Flower White, tiny, fuzzy balls about ½″ across.

Flowering Season April and May.

Fruit Reddish brown, thin, flat pod to 5″ long. Fall.

Soil & Moisture Will grow well on dry rockland.

pH Preference 5.5 to 7.5.

Salt Tolerance Excellent (1st line).

Freezes at about 32°F.

Rate of Growth Moderately fast.

Propagation Seeds.

Culture No special care required. *L. latisiliqua,* 30′ x 25′, is available in south Florida.

Problems No serious problems. Rust disease. Stem galls.

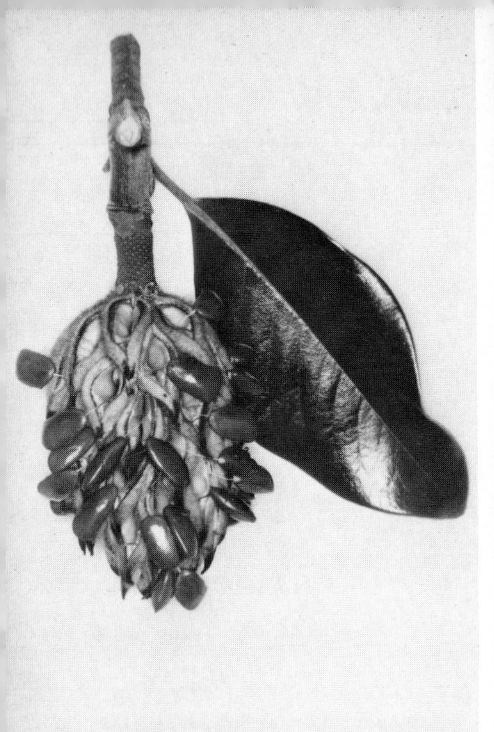

Scientific Name *Magnolia grandiflora* **Common Name** SOUTHERN MAGNOLIA

Family Magnoliaceae **Approx. Height** 80′ **Width** 45′

Native to North Carolina to Florida and Texas.

Habit of Growth Upright, pyramidal tree with a dense head.

Description Leaves evergreen, alternate, simple, stiff, oval, pointed, to 8″ long. Glossy, dark green above and brown, tomentose below.

Landscape Use Specimen, framing, background, avenue, and park.

Flower White, waxy, about 8″ across. Fragrant.

Flowering Season Mostly April & May.

Fruit Cone-like to 4″ long. Red seeds. Birds eat them.

Soil & Moisture Prefers deep, enriched soil with adequate moisture.

pH Preference 5.5 to 6.5.

Salt Tolerance Fair (2nd line).

Freezes at about Hardy.

Rate of Growth Moderate.

Propagation Seeds, cuttings, and graftings. Trees from cuttings and graftings flower sooner & have superior shape.

Culture Use mulch and acid fertilizer. Do not disturb soil around tree. Named cultivars available which vary in height, shape, and leaf size. Note: *M. virginiana* has smaller, white blossoms and thinner leaves that are silvery below, to 6″.

Problems Algal leaf spot disease. Scales. Takes several years to become established after transplanting.

Scientific Name *Melaleuca quinquenervia (M. leucadendra)*

Common Name PUNK TREE CAJEPUT or CAJUPUT

Family Myrtaceae

Approx. Height 50′ **Width** 20′

Native to Australia.

Habit of Growth Upright tree with rather large trunk and whitish, shaggy, thick, spongy bark that sheds easily.

Description Leaves evergreen, alternate, simple, grayish green, stiff, narrow at both ends, to 4″ long and ¾″ wide. Crushed leaves aromatic.

Landscape Use Specimen, framing, skyline, screen, tall hedge, avenue, and windbreak.

Flower Creamy, "bottle-brush" spikes to 6″ long.

Flowering Season Some most of the year.

Fruit Brown, round, woody capsules about ⅛″ across surround stems.

Soil & Moisture Tolerant of most soils.

pH Preference 5.5 to 6.5.

Salt Tolerance Fair (2nd line).

Freezes at about 26°F.

Rate of Growth Fast.

Propagation Seeds.

Culture Easy to grow. Can be pruned to any shape.

Problems Root rot disease. Scales and twig girdlers. Roots vigorous. Should not be planted near valuable plants. A pest when it escapes. Some people are allergic to its pollen.

Scientific Name *Melia azedarach*

Common Name CHINABERRY
PRIDE-OF-INDIA

Family Meliaceae

Approx. Height 60′ **Width** 40′

Native to Southern Asia.

Habit of Growth Symmetrical, umbrella-shaped, dense tree with thick trunk and furrowed bark.

Description Leaves mostly deciduous, alternate, odd-bipinnately compound with dark green, toothed leaflets with long untoothed tips, to about 3″ long.

Landscape Use Specimen, background, and shade.

Flower Purplish, small, in panicles 4″ to 8″ long. Fragrant.

Flowering Season Spring.

Fruit Yellow, roundish drupe to ¾″ across. Persistent.

Soil & Moisture Very tolerant of most soils.

pH Preference 5.5 to 7.5.

Salt Tolerance Poor (3rd line).

Freezes at about Hardy.

Rate of Growth Fast.

Propagation Seeds and cuttings.

Culture Easy to grow. Compact cultivars are available.

Problems Whitefly and scales. Grass will not grow under it. Fruit poisonous.

Scientific Name *Moringa pterygosperma (M. oleifera)* **Common Name** HORSERADISH TREE

Family Moringaceae **Approx. Height** 25′ **Width** 25′

Native to India.

Habit of Growth Small, open tree with flaky, corky, light gray bark.

Description Leaves evergreen, tripinnately compound, fern-like, 1′ to 3′ long with dull green, thin, variable leaflets that are larger at tips than are the other leaflets.

Landscape Use Specimen, framing, hedge, pot or urn.

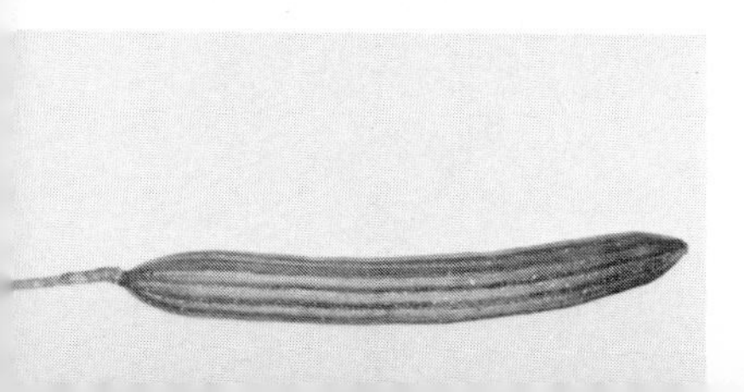

Flower White, to 1″ across, in loose, showy clusters. Fragrant.

Flowering Season All year.

Fruit Light brown, roundish, 3-sided, mature capsule to 18″ long and 1″ across with winged seeds. Edible when young.

Soil & Moisture Tolerant of most soils.

pH Preference 5.5 to 7.5.

Salt Tolerance Poor (3rd line).

Freezes at about 32°F.

Rate of Growth Moderate.

Propagation Seeds and cuttings.

Culture Easy to grow. Roots have a horseradish flavor.

Problems No serious pests.

Scientific Name *Myrica cerifera* **Common Name** SOUTHERN WAX MYRTLE
SOUTHERN BAYBERRY

Family Myricaceae **Approx. Height** 30′ **Width** 20′

Native to New Jersey to Texas, Florida and Bahamas.

Habit of Growth Tall shrub or small tree with irregular, spreading branches.

Description Leaves evergreen, alternate, simple, olive green, crisp, narrow oblanceolate, crinkled along edges, irregularly toothed, to 4″ long. Leaves, berries, and stems aromatic.

Landscape Use Background, screen, hedge, and seaside.

Flower Inconspicuous catkins. Dioecious.

Flowering Season Winter.

Fruit Grayish, waxy, ⅛″ drupes on stem. Winter.

Soil & Moisture Tolerant of wet and dry conditions.

pH Preference 5.0 to 6.0.

Salt Tolerance Excellent (1st line).

Freezes at about Hardy.

Rate of Growth Slow.

Propagation Seeds, suckers, and transplanting from the woods with permission.

Culture Prune to shape. Stands shearing well.

Problems Leaf spot and dieback diseases. Caterpillars.

Scientific Name *Noronhia emarginata*

Common Name MADAGASCAR OLIVE

Family Oleaceae

Approx. Height 30′ **Width** 20′

Native to Madagascar.

Habit of Growth Upright, small tree with open top and slender branches.

Description Leaves evergreen, simple, opposite to whorled, gray-green, leathery, obovate, notched at tip, edges turned under, to 7″ long.

Landscape Use Specimen, framing, avenue, and seaside. Wherever a small tree is desired.

Flower Yellowish, small, in clusters.

Flowering Season Spring and summer.

Fruit Purple, roundish drupe, 1 ¼″ long. Fall. Edible.

Soil & Moisture Widely tolerant—beach sand to clay.

pH Preference 5.5 to 7.5.

Salt Tolerance Excellent (1st line).

Freezes at about 30° F.

Rate of Growth Moderate.

Propagation Seeds, cuttings, and air layerings.

Culture More wind and salt tolerant than sea grape.

Problems Few. Scales.

Scientific Name *Pandanus utilis* **Common Name** COMMON SCREW-PINE

Family Pandanaceae **Approx. Height** 30′ **Width** 20′

Native to Madagascar.

Habit of Growth Tree with stilt-like prop roots and many branches.

Description Leaves evergreen, strap-like, bluish green with reddish spines on margins and midrib, to 3′ long and 3″ wide.

Landscape Use Specimen, patio, pot or urn.

Flower Dioecious. Male: showy, 18″ racemes at end of branches. Female: non colorful, ball-like flowers hanging from branches.

Flowering Season Spring.

Fruit Green turning yellow, roundish, rough, compound syncarp to 6″ across with prism-like sections.

Soil & Moisture Tolerant of most soils.

pH Preference 5.5 to 7.5.

Salt Tolerance Excellent (1st line).

Freezes at about 32°F.

Rate of Growth Slow.

Propagation Seeds and cuttings.

Culture Little care is needed after it is established.

Problems Leaf spot disease. Scales. Old leaves are a nuisance.

Scientific Name *Parkinsonia aculeata* **Common Name** JERUSALEM THORN

Family Leguminosae **Approx. Height** 25′ **Width** 20′

Native to Tropical America.

Habit of Growth Small, loose, open, thorny tree with green twigs and branches that zigzag and droop.

Description Leaves deciduous, alternate, pinnately compound and look like flattened twigs, to 16″ long with numerous, small leaflets.

Landscape Use Specimen, framing, skyline, and avenue. Seasonal color.

Flower Showy, yellow, pea-shaped, 1″ across, in racemes. Fragrant.

Flowering Season Mostly March to May.

Fruit Dark brown, flat, leathery pod to 6″ long. Pod is constricted between seeds.

Soil & Moisture Tolerant of drought and poor soils.

pH Preference 5.5 to 7.5.

Salt Tolerance Fair (2nd line).

Freezes at about Hardy.

Rate of Growth Fast.

Propagation Seeds and cuttings.

Culture Prune to shape. Responds to fertilizer.

Problems Thorns. Root rot disease. Scales and caterpillars. Nematodes.

Scientific Name *Peltophorum pterocarpum (P. inerme)* **Common Name** YELLOW POINCIANA

Family Leguminosae **Approx. Height** 60′ **Width** 40′

Native to India to Australia.

Habit of Growth Tree with spreading top.

Description Leaves deciduous, bipinnately compound, to 1½′ long, fern-like, with rusty, velvety pubescent, oblong leaflets to ¾″ long.

Landscape Use Specimen, framing, background, shade, avenue, park, and large, open areas. Seasonal color.

Flower Showy, bright yellow, to 1½″ wide, in erect panicles to 12″ long, above the foliage. Fragrant.

Flowering Season May to September.

Fruit Reddish turning black, woody pod, flat and winged, to 4″ long. Late summer and fall.

Soil & Moisture Flowers best on well-drained soil.

pH Preference 5.5 to 7.0.

Salt Tolerance Fair (2nd line).

Freezes at about 28°F.

Rate of Growth Fast.

Propagation Seeds and cuttings.

Culture Easy to grow. Drought tolerant.

Problems Surface roots. Not wind resistant.

Scientific Name *Pinus elliottii* var. *densa* **Common Name** SOUTH FLORIDA SLASH PINE

Family Pinaceae **Approx. Height** *70′* **Width** 30′

Native to South Florida and coasts of central Florida.

Habit of Growth Upright tree usually with dense, symmetrical head.

Description Leaves evergreen, glossy, dark green needles in sheaths of 2 or 3, 7″ to 12″ long.

Landscape Use Specimen, park, roadside, and naturalistic plantings. For light shade.

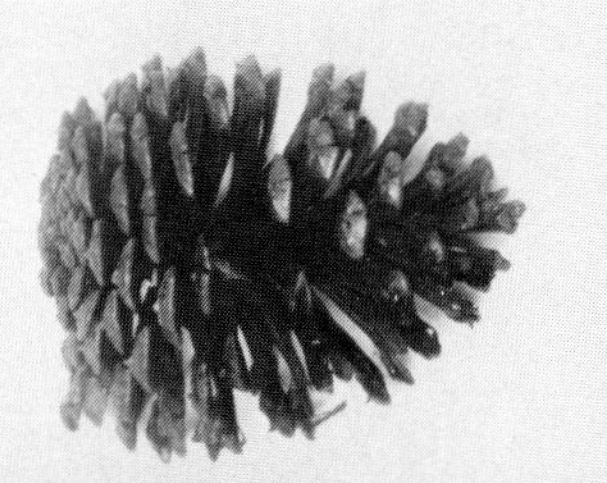

Flower Inconspicuous on tips of branches.

Flowering Season Spring.

Fruit Reddish brown, typical pine cone, to 7″ long with short, curved prickle near tip of each scale.

Soil & Moisture Well-drained, sandy soil.

pH Preference 5.5 to 7.5.

Salt Tolerance Fair (2nd line).

Freezes at about Hardy.

Rate of Growth Moderate.

Propagation Seeds.

Culture Easy to grow.

Problems Blight and canker diseases. Bark beetles, sawflies, and borers. Will not tolerate traffic, fill, or other abuse above root system.

Scientific Name *Platanus occidentalis* **Common Name** EASTERN SYCAMORE
BUTTONWOOD
AMERICAN PLANE

Family Platanaceae **Approx. Height** 125′ **Width** 100′

Native to Maine to Minnesota and south to Texas and Florida.

Habit of Growth Tree with broad, open head and straight trunk which sheds its bark in strips. Old tree trunks have mottled appearance.

Description Leaves deciduous, alternate, simple, greenish yellow, 3 to 5 palmately lobed with toothed edges, 4″ to 10″ across.

Landscape Use Background, shade, avenue, park, and large, open areas.

Flower Inconspicuous. Dense, ball-like clusters.

Flowering Season Spring.

Fruit Round, woody balls, 1½″ across.

Soil & Moisture Tolerant of most soils. Prefers enriched, moist soil.

pH Preference 5.5 to 7.5.

Salt Tolerance Fair (2nd line).

Freezes at about Hardy.

Rate of Growth Moderate.

Propagation Seeds.

Culture Grows best in central and northern parts of Florida. Minimum care once it is established.

Problems Leaves become brown due to lace bugs and mites. Leaves are a nuisance.

Scientific Name *Platycladus orientalis (Thuja orientalis)* **Common Name** ORIENTAL ARBOR-VITAE

Family Cupressaceae **Approx. Height** 40′ **Width** 20′

Native to North China and Korea.

Habit of Growth Pyramidal or globular tree with dense foliage and reddish brown bark.

Description Leaves evergreen, opposite, in pairs at right angles, medium green, tiny, scale-like, on vertical, flattened branchlets. Foliage fragrant.

Landscape Use Specimen, screen, and large, open areas.

Flower Inconspicuous.

Flowering Season Spring.

Fruit Inconspicuous cone, with spines, to 1″. Winter.

Soil & Moisture Any well-drained soil.

pH Preference 5.5 to 7.0.

Salt Tolerance Poor (3rd line).

Freezes at about Hardy.

Rate of Growth Moderately fast.

Propagation Cuttings.

Culture Easy to grow. Some cultivars have bluish or yellowish foliage.

Problems Juniper blight and dieback diseases. Scales. Mites. Often planted too close to houses. Large trees are hard to transplant.

Scientific Name *Plumeria rubra f. acutifolia* **Common Name** MEXICAN FRANGIPANI

Family Apocynaceae **Approx. Height** 20′ **Width** 20′

Native to Mexico.

Habit of Growth Stocky tree with spreading crown and thick, fleshy branches.

Description Leaves deciduous, alternate, simple, lance-shaped, stiff and leathery, to 15″ long. Leaves in clusters at end of branches.

Landscape Use Specimen, border, and patio. For tropical effect.

Flower Whitish or yellowish usually with yellow centers, waxy, 2″ across, in clusters. Fragrant.

Flowering Season Spring and summer.

Fruit Twin pods with winged seeds.

Soil & Moisture Well-drained soil. Will not stand wet feet.

pH Preference 5.5 to 7.5.

Salt Tolerance Fair (2nd line).

Freezes at about 32°F.

Rate of Growth Moderate.

Propagation Cuttings. Dry them in the shade before planting.

Culture Easy to grow. Improve soil prior to planting. There are several frangipanis with flowers varying from yellow to rose.

Problems Rust disease should be controlled. Nematodes. Milky sap is irritating if left on skin.

Scientific Name *Podocarpus macrophyllus var. Maki* **Common Name** YEW PODOCARPUS

Family Podocarpaceae **Approx. Height** 40′ **Width** 15′

Native to Japan.

Habit of Growth Dense, upright tree.

Description Leaves evergreen, alternate, simple, linear, with large midrib, to 4″ long and ¼″ wide. Green above and lighter green below.

Landscape Use Specimen, screen, and tall hedge. Trimmed for foundation plantings. One of Florida's most versatile plants.

Flower Inconspicuous. Female flowers greenish. Dioecious.

Flowering Season Spring and summer.

Fruit Purplish, egg-shaped, to ½″ long. Edible aril. Birds eat them.

Soil & Moisture Prefers well-drained, enriched soil.

pH Preference 5.5 to 7.0.

Salt Tolerance Fair (2nd line).

Freezes at about Hardy.

Rate of Growth Moderate.

Propagation Seeds and cuttings. Mist soft wood cuttings in summer.

Culture Tolerates shade.
Note: *P. nagi, P. gracilior* and *P. elongatus* and other species are available.

Problems Root rot and leaf spot diseases. Scales. Nematodes. Difficult to transplant when large. Pollen and fruit are a nuisance.

Scientific Name *Pongamia pinnata* **Common Name** PONGAM
POONGA-OIL TREE

Family Leguminosae **Approx. Height** 40′ **Width** 40′

Native to Tropical Asia and Australia.

Habit of Growth Spreading tree with somewhat drooping branches.

Description Leaves briefly deciduous, alternate, pinnately compound with 5 to 7 glossy green, ovate leaflets to about 4″ long. Strong odor when crushed.

Landscape Use Specimen, framing, shade, avenue, and windbreak.

Flower White, pink, or lavender, pea-like, in racemes to 10″ long.

Flowering Season Spring.

Fruit Brown, flat, woody, oval pods to 1½″ long with one seed. Seed poisonous.

Soil & Moisture Prefers well-drained, enriched soil.

pH Preference 5.5 to 7.5.

Salt Tolerance Fair (2nd line).

Freezes at about 30°F.

Rate of Growth Fast.

Propagation Seeds.

Culture Little care required once it is established.

Problems Caterpillars. Leaves and pods are a nuisance.

Scientific Name *Prunus caroliniana (Laurocerasus caroliniana)* **Common Name** CHERRY LAUREL

Family Rosaceae **Approx. Height** 40′ **Width** 20′

Native to North Carolina to Florida and Texas.

Habit of Growth Small tree with dense, rounded top.

Description Leaves evergreen, alternate, simple, oblong-lanceolate with few marginal teeth, 2″ to 4″ long. Glossy, dark green above and paler below. Leaves have a bitter taste; poisonous when wilted.

Landscape Use Screen, hedge, shade, avenue and park. Excellent for topiary effect. Wherever a medium sized tree is desired.

Flower Whitish, about 1/8″ across, in dense racemes. Fragrant.

Flowering Season Spring.

Fruit Dark purple, ovate drupes about 1/2″ long. Birds eat them.

Soil & Moisture Well-drained, enriched soil.

pH Preference 5.0 to 6.5.

Salt Tolerance Poor (3rd line).

Freezes at about Hardy.

Rate of Growth Moderate.

Propagation Seeds and suckers.

Culture Easy to grow. It will grow in sun or shade. It can be pruned to any shape.

Problems Stem canker disease. Caterpillars. Mites. Dense shade and vigorous roots prevent grass from growing. Seedlings are a nuisance.

Scientific Name *Pseudobombax ellipticum (Pachira fastuosa)* **Common Name** SHAVING-BRUSH TREE

Family Bombacaceae **Approx. Height** 30′ **Width** 30′

Native to Tropical America.

Habit of Growth Asymmetrical, open, spreading tree with smooth, green trunk.

Description Leaves deciduous, palmately compound with 5 to 7, light green, oblong to obovate leaflets to 9″ long. Foliage sparse. Stems greenish streaked with gray.

Landscape Use Specimen and background.

Flower Showy, pink or white stamens, 5 petals curled back, to about 6″. Solitary.

Flowering Season Late winter and spring.

Fruit Leathery, 5-valved capsule, 6″ by 1¾″. (None in Florida.)

Soil & Moisture Moist, enriched soil.

pH Preference 5.5 to 7.5.

Salt Tolerance Poor (3rd line).

Freezes at about 30°F.

Rate of Growth Moderate.

Propagation Cuttings.

Culture Little care is needed after it is established.

Problems Scales. Mites. Leaves and flowers are a nuisance.

Scientific Name *Quercus laurifolia* **Common Name** LAUREL OAK

Family Fagaceae **Approx. Height** 75′ **Width** 40′

Native to Virginia to Florida and Louisiana.

Habit of Growth Symmetrical, upright tree with dense, round top and ascending branches.

Description Leaves tardily deciduous, alternate, simple, smooth, narrowly elliptic and variable, to 5″ long. Shining green above and pale below.

Landscape Use Specimen, shade, avenue, and park. Most popular oak.

Flower Inconspicuous catkins.

Flowering Season Spring.

Fruit Globose acorns, ½″ long. Shallow cups cover ¼ of nuts. Birds eat them.

Soil & Moisture Tolerant. Will grow in most good soils.

pH Preference 5.5 to 6.5.

Salt Tolerance Poor (3rd line).

Freezes at about Hardy.

Rate of Growth Moderate to fast.

Propagation Seeds.

Culture Little care is needed after it is established.

Problems Mushroom root rot and leaf blister diseases. Galls. Too large for small lot.

Scientific Name *Quercus virginiana* **Common Name** LIVE OAK

Family Fagaceae **Approx. Height** 60′ **Width** 90′

Native to Virginia to Florida and Mexico.

Habit of Growth Tree with thick, grooved trunk and wide-spreading branches.

Description Leaves evergreen, alternate, simple, leathery, shape variable, to 5″ long. Shining, dark green above, pale below. Leaves slightly curved under at margins.

Landscape Use Specimen, background, shade, avenue, and park.

Flower Inconspicuous catkins.

Flowering Season Spring.

Fruit Blackish, oblong acorns, ¾″ long. Cups cover ⅓ of nuts. Birds eat them.

Soil & Moisture Prefers moist, enriched soil.

pH Preference 5.5 to 6.5.

Salt Tolerance Fair (2nd line).

Freezes at about Hardy.

Rate of Growth Fast growing if given good care.

Propagation Seeds.

Culture Easy to grow. Transplants with ease. Wind resistant.

Problems Mushroom root rot and leaf blister diseases. Galls. Spanish moss. Too large for average lot.

Scientific Name *Ravenala madagascariensis* **Common Name** TRAVELER'S TREE

Family Strelitziaceae **Approx. Height** 25′ **Width** 15′

Native to Madagascar.

Habit of Growth Symmetrical, tree-like plant with sturdy, palm-like trunk topped with banana-like leaves.

Description Leaves evergreen, alternate, simple, medium green, to 10′ long and to 1½′ wide, give a fan-like appearance.

Landscape Use Specimen for tropical effect, pot or urn.

Flower Whitish, small, held erect in canoe-like bracts.

Flowering Season Summer.

Fruit Woody, 3-celled, banana-shaped, capsule to 4″ long with black seeds covered with indigo arils.

Soil & Moisture Enriched, well-drained but moist soil.

pH Preference 5.5 to 6.5.

Salt Tolerance Poor (3rd line).

Freezes at about 30°F. Often comes back.

Rate of Growth Fast.

Propagation Seeds and occasionally by suckers.

Culture Prune to remove damag leaves.

Problems Cercospora leaf spot ease. Wind will shred leaves

Scientific Name *Salix babylonica* **Common Name** WEEPING WILLOW

Family Salicaceae **Approx. Height** 35′ **Width** 35′

Native to China.

Habit of Growth Open, medium sized tree with long, weeping branches.

Description Leaves deciduous, alternate, simple, lanceolate, serrate to 6″ long. Grayish green below.

Landscape Use Specimen, framing, border, and in aquatic situations.

Flowers Inconspicuous catkins. Dioecious.

Flowering Season Spring and fall.

Fruit Small, 2-valved capsule.

Soil & Moisture Any moist soil.

pH Preference 5.5 to 7.0.

Salt Tolerance Poor (3rd line).

Freezes at about Hardy.

ate of Growth Fast.

Cuttings of any conven-

generally short lived,

s, scales, and borers.

oorly along east coast

Scientific Name *Sapium sebiferum* **Common Name** CHINESE TALLOW TREE

Family Euphorbiaceae **Approx. Height** 30′ **Width** 20′

Native to China and Japan.

Habit of Growth Tree with upright trunk, long, slender branches and open top.

Description Leaves deciduous, alternate, simple, somewhat heart-shaped, to 3″ long with long, slender petiole. Leaves turn yellow to red in the fall. Milky sap.

Landscape Use Specimen, framing, shade, avenue, and park. Wherever a small tree is desired.

Flower Inconspicuous. Yellow, in terminal spikes, 2″ to 4″ long.

Flowering Season Spring and early summer.

Fruit Hard, 3-lobed capsule, ½″ across, with 3 large, white seeds.

Soil & Moisture Tolerant of most soils. Grows well in moist or dry soils.

pH Preference 5.5 to 7.5.

Salt Tolerance Poor (3rd line).

Freezes at about Hardy.

Rate of Growth Moderate to fast.

Propagation Seeds, cuttings, and sometimes graftings.

Culture Easy to grow. Naturalized in northwest Florida.

Problems Few. Root rot and leaf spot diseases.

Scientific Name *Schinus terebinthifolius*

Common Name BRAZILIAN PEPPER TREE

Family Anacardiaceae

Approx. Height 30′ **Width** 30′

Native to Brazil.

Habit of Growth Large shrub or pruned to small, dense, bushy, spreading tree.

Description Leaves evergreen, alternate, odd-pinnately compound, 4″ to 8″ long. Leaflets usually 7, coarse, oblong, sessile, to 3″ long. Dark green above, lighter below. Aromatic.

Landscape Use Specimen, screen, hedge, and patio.

Flower Inconspicuous. White, in dense clusters. Dioecious.

Flowering Season Spring and summer.

Fruit Showy, bright red, round drupes, ⅛″ across. Winter. Birds eat them.

Soil & Moisture Tolerant of most soils. Prefers well-drained, enriched soil.

pH Preference 5.5 to 7.5.

Salt Tolerance Fair (2nd line).

Freezes at about 22°F.

Rate of Growth Fast.

Propagation Seeds. Cuttings from female plants will produce trees that will have berries.

Culture Easy to grow. Full sun is best. Prune to shape.

Problems Scales and foliage thrips. Mites. Can become a weed tree. Bloom may cause skin rash and respiratory irritation to susceptible people.

Scientific Name *Spathodea campanulata* **Common Name** AFRICAN TULIP-TREE

Family Bignoniaceae **Approx. Height** 50′ **Width** 30′

Native to Tropical Africa.

Habit of Growth Large, tall, erect tree with narrow, dense crown and furrowed trunk.

Description Leaves evergreen, opposite, pinnately compound to 1½′ long. Leaflets 9 to 19, medium green, elliptic to ovate, 2″ to 5″ long.

Landscape Use Specimen, framing, background, shade, and avenue.

Flower Showy, orange-scarlet, tulip-like, about 4″ long and 2″ wide, in clusters usually above the foliage.

Flowering Season Midwinter into July.

Fruit Brown, smooth, woody capsule, narrowed at each end, about 8″ long and 2″ wide with small, white, winged seeds.

Soil & Moisture Prefers well-drained, enriched soil.

pH Preference 5.5 to 7.0.

Salt Tolerance Fair (2nd line).

Freezes at about 32°F.

Rate of Growth Fast.

Propagation Seeds and cuttings.

Culture Easy to grow once it is established. A yellow-flowered cultivar is available.

Problems Few. Damaged by strong winds.

Scientific Name *Swietenia mahagoni* **Common Name** MAHOGANY

Family Meliaceae **Approx. Height** 50′ **Width** 35′

Native to South Florida, Bahamas, and West Indies.

Habit of Growth Slender, upright tree with reddish brown trunk and compact, rounded crown.

Description Leaves briefly deciduous, alternate, even-pinnately compound, 4″ to 8″ long. Leaflets, 6 to 10, leathery, elliptic to ovate with pointed tips, to 4″ long. Shining, dark green above and yellow to brown below.

Landscape Use Framing, shade, avenue, park, and seaside.

Flower Inconspicuous. Tiny, white to greenish, in panicles 2″ to 6″ long.

Flowering Season Spring and summer.

Fruit Brown, ovoid, woody capsule to 5″ long with winged seeds about 2″ long.

Soil & Moisture Most soils but prefers hammock soils.

pH Preference 5.5 to 7.0.

Salt Tolerance Excellent (1st line).

Freezes at about 32°F.

Rate of Growth Moderate to fast.

Propagation Seeds.

Culture Responds to good care. Grass will grow under it. Wind resistant.

Problems Leaf spot disease. Tent caterpillars and stem borers.

Scientific Name *Tabebuia argentea*

Common Name SILVER TRUMPET TREE
TREE-OF-GOLD

Family Bignoniaceae

Approx. Height 25′ **Width** 15′

Native to Paraguay and Argentina.

Habit of Growth Asymmetrical, open tree with often crooked trunk and rough, light gray, corky bark.

Description Leaves deciduous, palmately compound with 5 to 7, silvery-gray, narrow leaflets to 6″ long, clustered at the tips of branches.

Landscape Use Specimen, framing, patio, and avenue.

Flower Showy, yellow, trumpet-shaped, to 2½″ long, in terminal clusters. Fragrant.

Flowering Season Spring, before the leaves.

Fruit Gray with black streaks, oblong, woody capsule to 6″ long.

Soil & Moisture Tolerant of most soils. Stands drought.

pH Preference 5.5 to 7.0.

Salt Tolerance Fair (2nd line).

Freezes at about 28°F.

Rate of Growth Moderate.

Propagation Seeds, graftings, and air layerings.

Culture Young trees need support and training.

Problems Leaf spot, dieback, and rust diseases.

Scientific Name *Tabebuia pallida*

Common Name PINK TRUMPET TREE

Family Bignoniaceae

Approx. Height 25′ **Width** 15′

Native to West Indies.

Habit of Growth Small tree with a slender trunk and scaly bark.

Description Leaves evergreen or deciduous, palmately compound with 3 to 5, stiff, oblong to elliptic leaflets to 6″ long, arranged in whorls.

Landscape Use Specimen, framing, patio, and avenue.

Flower Pink to nearly white, trumpet-shaped, to 3″ long.

Flowering Season Spring.

Fruit Slender capsule to 1′ long.

Soil & Moisture Tolerant of most soils. Stands drought.

pH Preference 5.5 to 7.0.

Salt Tolerance Fair (2nd line).

Freezes at about 30°F.

Rate of Growth Moderate.

Propagation Seeds, graftings, and air layerings.

Culture Easy to grow. Should be used more.

Problems Leaf spot and rust diseases. Mites.

Scientific Name *Taxodium distichum* **Common Name** BALD CYPRESS

Family Taxodiaceae **Approx. Height** 80′ **Width** 35′

Native to Delaware to Florida and west to Arkansas and Texas.

Habit of Growth Young trees pyramidal; older trees irregularly flat topped and with light brown, furrowed bark. "Knees" frequent in wet situations; trunk larger at base.

Description Leaves deciduous, alternate, light green, linear, about ½″ long.

Landscape Use Specimen, lakeside, park, and in naturalistic effect plantings.

Flower Inconspicuous.

Flowering Season Spring.

Fruit Globose cone, with woody scales, 1″ across.

Soil & Moisture Prefers wet situations. Will also grow on well-drained soils.

pH Preference 5.5 to 7.5.

Salt Tolerance Poor (3rd line).

Freezes at about Hardy.

Rate of Growth Moderate.

Propagation Seeds.

Culture Better growth can be expected if given some care.

Problems Few. Leaf spot and leaf blight diseases.

Scientific Name *Terminalia catappa* **Common Name** TROPICAL ALMOND

Family Combretaceae **Approx. Height** *55′* **Width** *35′*

Native to Malaya.

Habit of Growth Erect, symmetrical tree with horizontal branches in tiers.

Description Leaves deciduous, simple, glossy green, leathery, obovate, pointed, to 1′ long, clustered at the ends of twigs. Leaves turn bright red and fall during winter.

Landscape Use Specimen, shade, avenue, and seaside.

Flower Small, greenish white, in rat-tailed spikes to 6″ long.

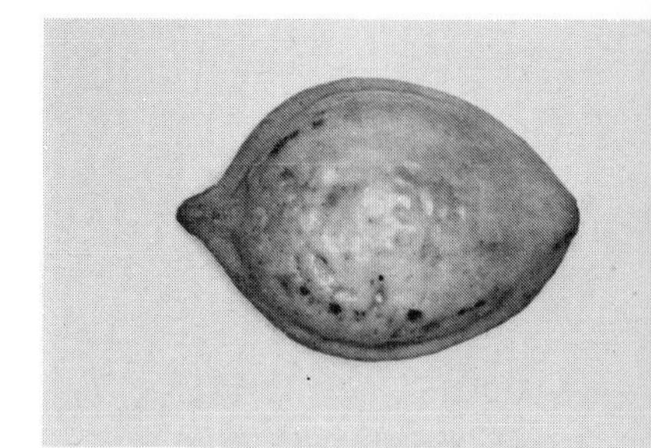

Flowering Season Spring.

Fruit Green to yellow or red, oval, winged drupe to about 2¼″ long. Fall. Edible.

Soil & Moisture Tolerant of most soils.

pH Preference *5.5 to 7.5.*

Salt Tolerance Excellent (1st line).

Freezes at about 30°F.

Rate of Growth Moderate to moderately fast.

Propagation Seeds.

Culture It should be mulched and fertilized. Wind resistant.

Problems No serious problems. Leaf spot disease. Old leaves and fruit are a nuisance.

Scientific Name *Thespesia populnea*

Common Name SEASIDE MAHOE
PORTIA TREE

Family Malvaceae

Approx. Height 35′ **Width** 30′

Native to Old World Tropics.

Habit of Growth Dense tree with round head and low, spreading branches.

Description Leaves evergreen, alternate, simple, heart-shaped, pointed, with long petioles, to about 5″ long and 3″ wide. The glossy green leaves have palmately net veins.

Landscape Use Specimen, framing, shade, avenue, and seaside.

Flower Hibiscus-like, yellow with purple-red center in the morning turning dark red as they fade in the afternoon, to 3″ across.

Flowering Season Spring and summer.

Fruit 5-lobed, leathery capsule to 1½″ across.

Soil & Moisture Tolerant of most soils and even of brackish water.

pH Preference 6.0 to 8.0.

Salt Tolerance Excellent (1st line).

Freezes at about 32°F.

Rate of Growth Moderately fast.

Propagation Seeds, cuttings, and air layerings.

Culture So well adapted to south Florida that it has escaped cultivation.

Problems No serious pests. Grass will not grow under it.

Scientific Name *Ulmus parvifolia* var. *sempervirens*

Common Name WEEPING ELM CHINESE ELM

Family Ulmaceae

Approx. Height 40′ **Width** 30′

Native to China and Japan.

Habit of Growth Spreading tree with an irregular, open head.

Description Leaves mostly evergreen, alternate, simple, glossy green, firm, elliptic to ovate, serrate, 1″ to 2½″ long.

Landscape Use Specimen, framing, shade, patio, and avenue.

Flower Inconspicuous. Whitish bracts, in clusters.

Flowering Season Late summer and fall.

Fruit Long, flat, winged samara about ⅓″ long.

Soil & Moisture Tolerant of most soils.

pH Preference 5.5 to 7.5.

Salt Tolerance Fair (2nd line).

Freezes at about Hardy.

Rate of Growth Moderate.

Propagation Seeds, cuttings, and air layerings.

Culture Prune to shape. Easy to grow.

Problems Leaf spot and twig dieback diseases. Sapsucker injury.

INDEX OF COMMON NAMES OF TREES AND PALMS

This book is arranged alphabetically according to the scientific names of the palms and then the other trees. This index is arranged alphabetically according to their common names.

Florida GARDEN GUIDE

OVER 2,750,000 PRINTED

Available from—

FREE IN MOST AREAS OF FLORIDA

Published in January, March, May, July, September, and November

PUBLISHED BY LEWIS S. MAXWELL, B.S.A. • 6230 TRAVIS BOULEVARD • TAMPA, FLORIDA 33610

WHAT TO DO IN YOUR GARDEN

In January

In Florida on some warm moist day in January, we often see our first flight of flying termites. Termites are a serious problem in the warm areas of the world.

If termites or suspicious insects are seen, call your termite specialist at once. Controlling termites in the modern home is difficult and complicated and can only be accomplished by a qualified professional termite exterminator.

To make your annual flowers bloom better and longer, you should remove the old flowers. Some of the flowers from your annuals should be cut and used in the house for decorations. Fresh flowers are so attractive and brighten up the home. This cutting of part of the flowers will also help your annual flower plants to bloom longer and better.

Ryegrass and Bermudagrass should have an extra fertilization in January. These grasses do not go dormant and so need this extra feeding to keep them healthy and green.

Continue to protect your cold sensitive plants.

Roses, peaches, and grapes **must** be pruned back when they are most dormant if they are to produce an abundance of flowers or fruit.

Those of you who want to set out dormant trees, shrubs, or vines should do this now before it is too late.

At last there is an apple that will do well in central Florida. It is called "Anna" and was developed in Israel. It requires only 200 to 400 hours of under 45°F. for good production. You or your nurseryman may be able to get some of these from the Grand Island Nursery, Grand Island, Florida 32726. This is the only source that I know.

IT CAN HAPPEN HERE!

"The budget should be balanced; the Treasury should be refilled; the public debt should be reduced; the arrogance of officialdom should be tempered and controlled. Assistance to foreign lands should be curtailed lest we become bankrupt. The mob should be forced to work and not depend upon government for subsistence."

Marcus Tullius Cicero in Rome between 106 and 43 B.C.

In February

Fertilize your citrus, other fruit, and shade trees as well as woody shrubs this month. Feeding them now will have the fertilizer elements available when the trees need them for their spring growth. This feeding is necessary if you are to have fruit or beauty from your trees.

In Florida with its poor sandy soils, there is no substitute for a quality fertilizer containing organics and added essential elements. Only a quality fertilizer will completely feed your plants.

If your bearing citrus trees need shaping, deadwood removed, or suckers cut out, this should be done before the flush of growth that produces the bloom. Don't wait as late pruning can hurt your next crop.

Citrus trees especially grapefruit should be sprayed with a neutral copper spray to prevent Melanose. Read the inside pages of this FLORIDA GARDEN GUIDE for information regarding some citrus diseases. Also read the article on fertilization and care of citrus in the book FLORIDA FRUIT.

Cut back your poinsettias when they start to look ragged. These cuttings can be used to start more plants.

Spring comes to Florida about the middle of February. At this time we can start planting our warm weather vegetables and annual flowers. Look on the back page to find a planting guide. We seldom have a hard freeze after February 15th.

TOMATO HORNWORM

The March/April FLORIDA GARDEN GUIDE will feature an article "The Insect Pests of Vegetables." It will also give controls.